POETIC VOYAGES BERKSHIRE

Edited by Helen Chatwin

First published in Great Britain in 2001 by
YOUNG WRITERS
Remus House,
Coltsfoot Drive,
Peterborough, PE2 9JX
Telephone (01733) 890066

HB ISBN 0 75433 102 4
SB ISBN 0 75433 103 2

FOREWORD

Young Writers was established in 1991 with the aim to promote creative writing in children, to make reading and writing poetry fun.

This year once again, proved to be a tremendous success with over 88,000 entries received nationwide.

The Poetic Voyages competition has shown us the high standard of work and effort that children are capable of today. It is a reflection of the teaching skills in schools, the enthusiasm and creativity they have injected into their pupils shines clearly within this anthology.

The task of selecting poems was therefore a difficult one but nevertheless, an enjoyable experience. We hope you are as pleased with the final selection in *Poetic Voyages Berkshire* as we are.

CONTENTS

Katie Handley Potts	64
Charlotte Keast	65
Sophie Totten	66
Francesca Robertson	66
Chantelle Rizan	67
Olivia McBain Morrish	67
Oriana Williams	68
Lucy Peacock	69
Becky Hunter	70
Harriet Riddick	70
Ellie May Holland	71
Charlotte Weeks	72
Eleanor Johnston	72
Kerry Gerdes-Hansen	73
Imogen Collins	74
Joanne Madeley	74
Leah Vellam-Steptoe	75
Nicola Bates	76
Myriam Frenkel	76
Lara Woodhead	77
Sophie Hunter	78
Cara Jewell	79
Chantelle Davison	80
Natalie Hyde	81
Clarisse Loughrey	82
Sophie Raine	82
Georgina Freestone	83

Finchampstead CE Primary School

Nicholas Payne	83
Becky Williams	84
Melissa Howe	84
Ben Hopkinson	85
Harvey Coles	85
Emma Osler	86
Sam Paulden	86
Amy Gray	87
Elizabeth Merritt	87

Vicky Briggs	88
Bradley Watmore	88
Rachna Joshi	89
Mathew Watmore	89
Sophie Barrow	90
Alex Gillett	90
Philip Saville	91
Michelle Robinson	91
Cressida Harris	92
Simon Annan	92
Danielle Wakefield-Piggott	93
Robert Row	93
Thomas Kennington	94
Jonathan Ellenby	94
Hayley Wilson	95
Niomi O'Rourke	96
William Malins	96
Lewis Gallagher	97
Katherine Lawrence	97
Marlene Maree	98
Julia Bedser	99

Francis Baily Primary School

Danniella O'Sullivan	99
Anna Beckett	100
William Endean	100
Rianna Marshall	101
Stewart Pearce	101
Rhiannon Duckett	102
Michael Panting	102
Victoria Kingston	102
James Ruczynski	103

Kintbury St Mary's School

Christopher Thomas	103
Alex Dixon	104
Jade Noden	104
Jack Bellmont	105

Zara Smith	105
Lucy Anstie	106
William Hutchins	106
Ellen Ireland	107
Stephanie Newland	107
Victoria Hemphill	108
Helen Rivett	108
Jack Thorp	109
Vicky Crook	109

Sandy Lane Junior School

Zoë Hammond	110
Jaun Burden	110
Sam Sweetzer	111
Jamie Osborn	111
Michelle Riordan	112
Martin Dixon	112
Matthew Bean	113
Joe Scantlebury	113
Christopher Merton	114
Ethan Fuller	114
Kelly Faulkner	115
Jessica Johnson	116
Rebecca Clayton	116
Jason Chung	117
Emily Hawkes	118
Martin Carpenter	118
Brendon Moss	119
Hannah Boon	119
Sadie Griffiths	120
Zachary Benham	120
Rhiannon Comerford	121
Tamsin Horne	121
Cally Trotman	122
Simone Platt	122
Robert Myers	123
Kirk Nevard	123
Stephanie Reynolds	124

The Poems

CHRISTMAS ACROSTIC

C   hristmas is when Jesus was born
H   is birthday is today
R   ight under the biggest star he was born
I   n a stable in Bethlehem
S   hepherds come to visit him
T   hree wise men as well
M   ary as his mother
A   nd Joseph as his father
S   ome people did not like him!

Emily Simms (8)
Brightwalton CE (Aided) Primary School

DANGERS OF WINTER

Black ice on the road
Danger! Danger! Say the signs
Icicles hanging off the bridge
River flooding all the homes
A blanket of snow on the ground
Let's go skating on the pond?
No! No! No!
The ice is too thin!
And I'm freezing.

Charlotte Wakelyn (10)
Brightwalton CE (Aided) Primary School

Snow

When I look up into the sky,
I realise the snow is starting to fly,
I see something cold, shivering and white,
Has landed on the end of my nose tonight,
In the darkness the snow is glowing,
Lighting my way to where I am going.

Emily Waters (9)
Brightwalton CE (Aided) Primary School

Winter

W inter is fun and ready for games
I t has no colour just blankets of snow
N othing matters except snow and your friends
T he scarves and the coats that people wear are lovely
and warm up on the fresh air.
E veryone's warm and laughing with glee
R ecreating the fun that we had last week.

Matthew Lawes (10)
Brightwalton CE (Aided) Primary School

Holding My Cousin

When I was holding my baby cousin
It felt all squidgy
She was very heavy
Her head was all floppy and very cuddly
I like my baby cousin
She cries very loud every time
She wants her food.

Sarah Bunn (8)
Brightwalton CE (Aided) Primary School

WINTER

My favourite time of year,
It really is so clear
I love winter so much,
It has that special touch
When it comes around,
It's lovely I'm sure I've found
I love the snow
So outside I must go!

Katie Hoyle (10)
Brightwalton CE (Aided) Primary School

REMEMBER THE WINTER

Winter is here,
Icicles are hanging,
Snow is falling everywhere,
A white blanket covers the green grass,
Evergreens are turning forever white,
Making sure you never forget the winter that covers the earth.

Rose Andrews (9)
Brightwalton CE (Aided) Primary School

SNOW

S   oft and fluffy,
N   ever hard,
O   n all the rooftops,
W   onderful times you can have.

Tom Stephens (11)
Brightwalton CE (Aided) Primary School

MY GRAN

My gran is happy as a white Christmas
Her hair is like cotton wool,
Her eyes are like sapphires,
Her face is like a squidgy balloon.
When she walks she is like a donkey,
When she sits she is like a mouse
When she laughs she's a monkey
When she sleeps she is like a mole in winter
The best thing about my gran is she's mine and not yours.

Ben Padwick (9)
Brightwalton CE (Aided) Primary School

VOYAGE TO AN UNKNOWN LAND

On my computer that's the key,
Is that witch calling me?
It's waving its arm and saying in a voice so high,
'Oh me, oh me, oh my!'

My eyes are closing, I feel funny,
I feel as though I'm in a pot of honey,
I've found myself in a strange land,
I'm glued tight in sinking sand.

I'm waving my arm and saying in a voice so high,
'Oh me, oh me, oh my!'
My eyes are closing once again,
I'm home and pleased I am!

Tiggy Joseph (10)
Chilton Foliat CE Primary School

THE VOYAGE

The highway man came trotting upon the purple moon,
With his horses hooves touching the floor,
'I'm after a goal tonight,
For how to target rich Richard is my plight.

I will go to his house,
And creep round like a mouse,
Then I will break in,
And my eyes will be as sharp as a pin,
I will steal his gold,
And I will not tell a soul.'

I got out of his house,
And again crept like a mouse,
The highway man came trotting, trotting
Along the purple moon.

Charlie Brown (11)
Chilton Foliat CE Primary School

THE VOYAGE

The roar of the T-rex blew us away
He blew us so far we were gone for a day
We saw a Stegosaur and he was a bore
He killed one of us and he would kill more
We heard the same old roar
We knew it wasn't the Stegosaur
We saw the T-rex who came from afar
Ahhh, we ran for the car
We drove off fast
And we were happy to be home at last.

Lewis Rose (11)
Chilton Foliat CE Primary School

THE VOYAGE

Over and over the dark misty sea,
All of my friends travelling with me.
So off I go on my around the sea trip
The waves are so huge compared to my ship.

Now I am nearly half way there,
Soon I will feel a breeze running through my hair
I have just seen some pea-green land,
I feel that I can touch it with my hand.

Now I am in this land,
I have touched it with my hand.
All of the people are really nice
I think for dinner, I'll have some rice.

I see a lion,
I like naming things, I'll call him Brian
There is a parrot
He is bright orange like a carrot.

The sunset is ever so radiant
I'll go home now back to Badiant.

Amy Woodham (9)
Chilton Foliat CE Primary School

A DREAM

A dream, a dream how nice it can be
Riding, riding in a car in the country out so far.
Racing down that country lane, oh wouldn't it be
Good if I had a little fame.
Oh where, oh where will this dream take me next,
To Santiago, wherever next?

The sea, the sea so blue, so blue
I have not got a clue what I want to do.
Go, go to see some trees and get some gigantic leaves
Make a big den sort of like a playpen.

Laura Sherwood (10)
Chilton Foliat CE Primary School

THE VOYAGE

I'm on my ship travelling to Spain,
But in my stomach there is a very bad pain,
I do not know if I will make it,
I think I will be OK for a little bit.
Waves crashing against my boat
I feel I need my furry warm coat!
Travelling across the rough blue sea,
It's getting rougher as it follows me.

Over the cloudy seas I go
Closer and closer to a glow,
Whatever it is I need to know!
Rushing towards it
I see it lit,
Just waiting for me,
Who is out at the sea,
There it is the little glow
I've found it, now I know,
That it is a little light
Just shining in the dark midnight.

Arabella Reeves (10)
Chilton Foliat CE Primary School

THE MAN ON THE MOON

The people on Earth were gasping
As the man on the Moon was dancing.

He was about to go back
When he saw an alien look at his pack.

He made friends with this alien, called Zog
Zog looked rather like a frog.

Zog said goodbye
And went up to the sky.

Ten, nine, eight, seven, six, five, four, three, two, one,
The man on the Moon was gone.

Henry Stapley (10)
Chilton Foliat CE Primary School

MY VOYAGE

I am floating along the sea
Just my boat and me,
If there's nothing I like more
Than just to see the sandy shore.

I look up at the sky
It seems to me that it's so high,
It's wonderful on the sea
With just my boat and me.

Amy Ward (10)
Chilton Foliat CE Primary School

THE VOYAGE

The ship was sailing, sailing
The sea was calling, calling,
The wind was singing, singing,
The voyage was beginning, beginning.

The spray was flying, flying,
The birds were crying, crying,
The waves were frothing, frothing,
The voyager was tossing, tossing.

The fish were hiding, hiding,
The men were deciding, deciding,
The nets were untying, untying,
The voyagers were relying, relying.

The quiet was springing, springing,
The nets were filling, filling,
The peace was ascending, ascending,
The voyage was ending, ending.

Charlotte Roots (10)
Chilton Foliat CE Primary School

THE VOYAGE

The waves were jumping,
Into the sky,
I even saw with my own two eyes.

The sea so blue like tears from the deep,
Floating along on a voyage of sleep.

Nadia Burrows (9)
Chilton Foliat CE Primary School

THE VOYAGE

The sea is rough,
The boat is tough.

Swish, swosh the sea sings,
The bell rings.

'It's the rage,'
The flattened shark is here,
As fast as a page.

The piercing scream of the wind,
Is here,
Water comes to your eyes,
We say it's a tear.

Fear, we feel, fear, fear,
The rage is really near.

We are there at the shore,
Our voyage is over,
Our voyage is over, over, over.

Jessica Preston (11)
Chilton Foliat CE Primary School

THE HISTORIC SURPRISE

The sea was silent,
The wind was calm,
The foam was like white horses leaping upon cloudy seas
But nobody was there to watch it
To hear it
Or to feel it.

There was a boat
Sunk under the water
But it started to rise and rise
The skeleton of the people follow
Like a shadow in my eyes
What a historic surprise.

Elizabeth Walley (9)
Chilton Foliat CE Primary School

THE ARCTIC

The snow lay pure and white upon the ground
The sun disappeared behind a cloud
The sky was dark with a misty gloom
The accident happened all too soon.

The huskies howled and yelped in fright
The wind was blowing with all its might
We slipped and slid further down and down
I was thinking of my small home town.

Suddenly we stopped slipping and sliding
The huskies and the sleigh stopped colliding
We collected our wits and began to climb
One of the huskies started to whine.

We clambered out of a monstrous pit
We were scared and shaken and trembled a bit
We sat on the sleigh and had a huge rest
Then we carried on, the huskies doing their best.

We arrived back at my small home town
It was sunset and the sun was going down
We were so tired we went straight to bed
The colours in the sky were glowing purple, orange and red.

Gemma Webb (10)
Chilton Foliat CE Primary School

THE VOYAGE

I'm in a plane in the sky,
Starting off not very high,
Looking out the window seeing all the fluffy clouds,
They are sticking together in separate crowds.

I want to get to India to see my family and friends,
Being in a plane, I can feel lots and lots of bends,
I hope I do get there soon,
Hopefully, well, before noon.

I'm travelling over seas and land,
Lots of beaches with lots of sand,
The sky devolves into a peachy sunset,
I'm glad I'm not at home in the weary wet.

There are a lot of people I have seen,
Some sound very nice, some sound very mean,
I have had lots of fun on my trip,
When I come back from India I can go by ship.

Rebecca Miles (10)
Chilton Foliat CE Primary School

THE VOYAGE

I feel the sea flowing by me
The shining blue twinkling in my eyes.
The silver in the dolphin shine
The smiling of the golden fish
I see it today, I will see it everyday
Until the time has come for me to say 'bye-bye'
I will come on the 17th August but come with me and I will go on.

Megan Ffoulkes (9)
Chilton Foliat CE Primary School

THE VOYAGE

No car, no boat, no plane have I,
A dragon is what I travel on
Its fiery breath has enough heat,
To melt an armoured car,
So scorching is its smoking tail it
Could turn a rock into magmar.

But he's my friend and always shall be,
Until his death he'll travel with me
In this fantasy world you won't know where you are,
But still my dragon and I travel afar.

Past goblins and ogres, anywhere we'll go,
Through rain, through sun and even through snow
But there comes a time when the journey must end,
And I have to say bye to my dragon friend.

Jamie Elsey (10)
Chilton Foliat CE Primary School

VOYAGE

A dream come true I'm going very, very soon.
I'm going on a bus, I'm going on a plane I must explain
Rushing, jumping everywhere without any care
Soon it will be time for me to go on the beach at Tobago
Mum and Dad are you ready, so let's go?
Oh no, where is my teddy bear
Is it already at Tobago?
Mum, Dad look there's a man over the road
Come on let's go.
Yes at last I'm going on holiday.

Stephen Allen (10)
Chilton Foliat CE Primary School

THE ABANDONED SHIP

On the Pacific Ocean the deep blue sea
Was covered with a thin white foamy spray,
The huge ship sailed slowly along disturbing the water,
The torn and ragged sails were blowing in the salty breeze.

The fish jumped up and down with eerie scales
Like a plate of shiny armour,
The water glistened in the twinkling light of the stars,
The nervous and worried pirates looked out in despair,
At miles and miles of ocean.

The crashing waves splashed against the rocks
And hit the faces of the abandoned pirates,
As the silver moon reflected on the waves surface
It sparkled in the eyes of the pirates,
Who were looking up at the night's sky.

The pirates looked out to an island covered with golden sand
And palm trees leaning over the water,
The pirate ship just glided past bobbing on the waves,
They should have stopped . . .

Jack Bishton (9)
Cranbourne Primary School

THE SHIP

On a sunny day
The silent sea gently rocked from side to side
The floorboards creaked and the killer whales squeaked
The peeled paint cracked and packed
The silent crew said 'Oh no.'

The captain said 'Doodly Do'
And the sea said 'Ssshhh'
And they all said 'Push'
And the sunny sun said 'Be careful.'

Rebecca Badley (9)
Cranbourne Primary School

SPACE JOURNEY

Still, everything quiet, desolate and deserted,
The eerie stillness of space
The blazing stars burning in the distance
This was it, the journey.
Through the small square windows.
The colossal and colourful rings of Saturn.
Bang! Something's gone wrong, gas vapour is forming
Out of the small square windows
Oh no. This is the Apollo 13 disaster again.
The eerie cold depths of *space*!
We were panicking
Space the final frontier!
Sad for our families, my son terrified.
Then the gas stopped
This was it.
We were dead.
But then a beautiful planet came into view we were saved
The crisis was over.

Maybe other life forms live there, we would be famous,
But then black, then a flash, a blinding light we were dead.
Our journey was over . . .

Jamie McKean (10)
Cranbourne Primary School

BEACH JOURNEY

I travelled on my feet,
Then I found my paradise,
I found the gentle flowing sea,
There were juicy green palm trees,
There were soft grains of yellow sand,
I saw colourful light shells,
And there were some shooting dolphins,
And the big noisy whales,
Juicy brown and white coconuts,
I dived into the slow waves,
I saw the fiery fishes,
And the slippery jellyfish,
And colourful bumpy star fish,
But greatest of all, the smooth silky pearls.

Beatrice Warner (10)
Cranbourne Primary School

THE CREW

As the shaky ship sailed
Scared crew try to get to the captain
The grumpy captain shouted
The crew kept crying and thought they were dying
They were flying, they heard the waves whine and whine.

The sail had a fall, they had seen land,
They saw something in the water, heading their way,
The captain started to shout 'Help, help, I'm dying'
On the sunny day they got to the land.

Ailsa Hunt (9)
Cranbourne Primary School

THE SEA TRIP

Under the waters green and cool,
The mermaids keep a swimming school,
The lobsters come and do a dance,
Then I see a dolphin glance,
The silky seaweed tickling my feet,
Then I felt the dancing beat,
I saw lots of coral shells,
Yes, I hear the ringing bells,
Swiftly swimming along the bay,
Isn't this a lovely day,
Now it's time to say goodbye
It's not as if I'm going to die,
Now it's time to go away,
Go on, go and play.

Rima Ben-Ghalia (10)
Cranbourne Primary School

THE SHIP

The foamy waves crashed against the deck,
The strong sailors tried to steer the ship away,
The crooked floorboards started to rattle,
The whirly wind started to blow,
The paint started to go rusty,
The salty sea started to go through the floorboards.

All the sailors had to think fast
The ship was sinking,
The tiny fish were screeching
The only choice the sailors had
Was to swim for it.

Joshua Paul (9)
Cranbourne Primary School

THE SHIP

The ship glided gently on its way,
On its way to nowhere,
The saggy sails drifting droopily
The thunder rolling across the heavens,
The wild wind howling like a ghost,
As the crew watched and wondered.

A luminous fork of lightning shot down,
Shot down to the foaming, wild waves
The voices of the sailors being whipped away,
As the wind carried them through the sapphire sky
No one knew what would happen next
As dead fish floated to the surface.

The wet, slippery planks started to rattle,
Began to rattle as the beautiful ship filled with water
The cargo was thrown dangerously around,
As the massive ship descended to its grave,
Its grave in the ocean,
The bottomless ocean.

Joe Denny (10)
Cranbourne Primary School

THE SHINY ROCKET

There was a shiny rocket that went to space
There was a shiny rocket that went to space
He travelled miles and miles to explore
The hotness coming out of the back
Seeing all the moon rocks on the moon
When they returned they were delighted
Delighted to get home so quick.

Billy Taylor (8)
Cranbourne Primary School

THE PLANE

The sapphire sky running past the window
Eric was listening to the happy hostess,
He put his hand past the chair
And felt around for his drink
He heard the whizzing winds running through the fluffy clouds
He had a funny feeling, the plane was vibrating
Tom heard the noisy motor
He looked through the window.

He looked through the window,
And heard a funny sound,
Oil spreading through the air,
And, and . . .
And getting ready to repair
The sun spreading through the blinds,
Nothing going to stop
In the last moments of his life
Boom, it dropped.

The gloomy sea is now polluted
Bodies on the ground,
Fish swimming through the plane
And now the submarine comes
To save bodies
But that was their grave,
All is one and one is all
All is dead.

Alexander Kay (9)
Cranbourne Primary School

IN THE AIR

In the high blue sky,
The fluffy birds lead the way
When the worried crew saw a dragon,
They began to cry
When they suddenly realised it was falling,
They flew down from the sky,
When they eventually found it was on the wing,
They knew it was on there,
For the aeroplane was tipping.

The exhausted dragon slipped and fell,
The worried crew turned red,
When the squashy controls froze,
The excited air hostess was worried,
When she heard a bang she looked down and saw the dragon
'Oh no' she cried
The birds had lead us,
The fluffy old birds have left us.

By the sun it was hot,
Some did not survive
I cried 'I will miss them'
Then the engine stopped 'Oh no!'

Sophie Botwright (8)
Cranbourne Primary School

BRIGHT BEACH

On a gorgeous bright beach,
The soft sand lay against my feet,
The lovely sea glittering ahead of me
Jellyfish wobbling and wibbling,
Camouflaged fish swimming around,
Diving dolphins jump up and down.

On a gorgeous bright beach
The screeching seagull hit my ear,
The tropical island under my eyes
I extremely enjoyed the day,
When I had run around and played,
Now this day is over,
I hope to come again some day.

Adryen Bayley (9)
Cranbourne Primary School

THE BIG VOYAGE CRASH

The people go whitling
The spaceship goes twirling
Around and around the shuttle goes,
Who knows where it is going to crash.

The shuttle is going to crash,
Ahhh the people scream, smash!
The spaceship is crumpled up,
What to do when they are stuck in slimy muck.

The people are knocked out,
There's no one about,
But one person who was an alien to help.

The alien helped the people,
The alien built the spaceship
So the people started the shuttle up,
The shuttle started to go,
The people went whirling
The spaceship went twirling
Around and around the shuttle goes.

Matthew Timms (10)
Cranbourne Primary School

THE SHIP

As the old wooden ship sailed through the salty sea
The wild wind began to howl
Slimy fish were jumping in and out of the waves
The soggy sails began to tear
As the stressed sailors walked up the dusty floorboards
The grumpy captain shouted in the wind
And his voice was snatched away.

As the thunder rolled over the sapphire sky
The crews voice drowned in the deafening wind
As a bolt of lightning struck on the boat
The old wooden planks began to crack.

As the old wooden planks began to crack
The stressed sailors began to worry
Their small mouths filled with salty water
And the big beautiful ship disappeared
In the dark everlasting sea.

Maxine Bradberry (9)
Cranbourne Primary School

THE JUNGLE

On this hot sunny day
The willing explorers saw,
The childish, cheating cheetah,
The talking tigers and more,
The jungle is such a scary place,
Nobody knows how it came,
The mischievous monkeys,
The sky high trees,
And perky parrots that play.

The slithery, sneaky snake,
The really boggy land,
The bouncy bushes,
The fluorescent flowers,
To be seen all they can,
The explorers saw the newest flowers,
In the jungle they came,
To see the new things on the land,
By foot they travelled all the way.

Claire Bailey (10)
Cranbourne Primary School

THE FISHING BOAT

A fifty foot wave flooded the deck,
The small fishing boat rocked about,
The captain called 'Get in here'
The explorer ran in roughly,
The soggy sails drooped suddenly
The both stopped and stared.

Suddenly the rough sea caused a whirlpool,
Which pulled the small boat down to the unexplored sand,
The heavy cargo slid from side to side in the cargo bay,
The small rusty boat had had its day, it was soon over,
The maple mast broke and fell into the bottomless sea,
Were they going to survive or not?

The explorer ran quickly to the cargo bay,
He took the biggest case and threw it
Threw it into the whirlpools darkest depths,
It closed over and it let go of the boat,
The boat took about five hours to get to the shore,
They made it, they weren't dead.

Fraser Deans (10)
Cranbourne Primary School

THE BOAT RIDE

As the shaky ship travelled the foamy Atlantic
A wild storm began to appear.
The worried explorers thought of a quick idea;
The sturdy ship began to turn to one side
As one of the explorers fell into the wavy Atlantic.

The explorers thought to go and try to steer the weak ship away,
As the others battled the vicious waves.
As the scaly fishes were pouncing out of the water
The boat was turning from side to side out of control.

As one of the brave explorers took on the wheel
The boat was back in their control
And so the explorers carried on their trip
With their weak ship.

Louise Sullivan (9)
Cranbourne Primary School

A SHIP VOYAGE

The creaky floorboards,
Vibrated through the sea
The dolphins jumped over the tattered sails
The cruel captain corrected the wooden wheel
The fish swam to hide in the seaweed
As the ship swam over, the sea went dark.

The jerking jellyfish
Trying to jump in a sailor's dish
The silent sea lets the boat float away
It might float on to a sand-set bay
Maybe it will happen again.

Sophie Bishton (9)
Cranbourne Primary School

WHAT ARE THEY?

Some are small, some are big,
Some live in water, some live on twigs!
Some are brown, some are blue,
Some are similar to me and you!

Some fly, some swim
Some are hers and some are hims!
Some are furry, some are cute,
Some make a sound like a flute!

Some are stripy, some are spotty,
Some of them drive you dotty!
Now what are they, can you guess?
It begins with an A and ends with an S!

Animals!

Rebecca Jayne Hill (8)
Falkland Primary School

RAPTORS

Raptors gradually start to attack,
And in the end they get a big smack,
Raptors are faster than a fast cheetah
And after their meal they drink a litre.

The two-legged beast,
Gets his large feast,
During the day,
In the middle of May.

Michael Thatcher (8)
Falkland Primary School

SNAILS

As slow as a slug they slither round and round,
Leaving shiny sparkling trails left behind them on the ground.

They are as quiet as a mouse,
As they trail up to the house.

They climb up the big tall wall,
And leave trails of slime over Dad's tools!

Rhonwen Lally (9)
Falkland Primary School

GUINEA PIGS

I have a pet,
That needs to go to the vet.

Jumping and pouncing around, makes him the best guinea pig
Ever to be found,
Every guinea pig runs round and round.

Cute and cuddly all the same, each one special in every way
And I get to play with him every day.

Lucy Jenkinson (9)
Falkland Primary School

RAPTORS

Raptor strikes, he bites his prey, he eats till the bone,
Cave men find the bone and stuff it with some foam
Raptors race cheetahs, once they've drunk a litre.
The two-legged beast, has his favourite feast.

Raptors stalk like a hulk
Raptor jumps over humps
As he jumps over hills, he sees fishes and their gills.

Craig Langley-Smith (9)
Falkland Primary School

COLOURS

Green is like
A thousand monsters
Mean and meaner
All from Mars.

Pink is like
A thousand roses
All tied up in
Bunches and posies.

Orange is as
Bright as the sun
All the children
Can have some fun.

Yellow is as soft
As sand spread
Across the
English land.

Black is dark
Dark as night
Everything is out of sight!

Katie Cook (9)
Falkland Primary School

THIS KID IN OUR SCHOOL

This kid in our class,
Just today he broke some glass!
Tomorrow he'll get into trouble,
But he knows what to do, he'll just grovel.

It comes to parent-teacher day,
Just the day before that we got to make stuff out of clay!
The teachers say,
Your son had a very bad day today!

Today he went to the head teacher
But not for bad work, for making a very good feature!
He said he worked his hardest, just a bit,
Because he got two stickers for it!

This boy at our school,
He popped our best football!
In our football match, a pin got stuck in his shoe!
He walked home and stepped in a load of poo!

He's the worst boy I've ever seen,
His house is never, ever clean.
No one would want to go to his house,
Because he has a snake and a pet mouse!

When it comes to lunch,
He would never have food in a big bunch
Once he started a food fight
But he went to our head teacher Mr Dwight.

Ben Pearce (8)
Falkland Primary School

KENYA THE LION CUB

Kenya is as bright as a daisy,
But also crazy!

As cuddly as a baby bear,
Mischievous as a little hare.

She is as beautiful as a kitten,
Once she has found her woollen mitten.

As rapid as a cheetah,
She runs a mile to join Blue Peter!

Sophie Anderson (9)
Falkland Primary School

A JOURNEY ACROSS THE DESERT

Walking through the desert
Is a tiring journey
You're hot and droopy
You're hungry a lot of the time
Your mouth is watering
You need water, water,
You're lost but determined
To get home safely
Without a cut or bruise on you
Forty days later
You're still determined to get home
A couple of days later
You succeed
It was a long, hard journey
But you succeeded!

Alexandra Wheeler (10)
Falkland St Gabriel's School

THE JOURNEY OF THE DEAD

White ghosts walking around,
Not a sound,
Silence.

Transparent shapes everywhere,
They wouldn't dare,
Escape.

They are trapped,
In mad thoughts,
Help.

Through that land,
Dead.

Running, panicking
Painfully crying,
Anger.

They escape,
With all their might,
Journey.

Journey through deserts,
All the wilderness,
Depression.

Through that land,
Dead.

They journey as the sun goes down,
They journey at the break of dawn,
They're desperate.

At last they come,
To the land of dreams,
Our Earth.

Hannah Mason (10)
Falkland St Gabriel's School

WAVES

Rolling, tumbling,
Crashing,
In the wind
This is the music waves make.

Calm, gentle
Small waves
In the breeze
This is the music waves make.

Bang, crash
Spray
On the rocks
This is the music waves make.

Waves rolling,
Softly
On the sea shore
This is the music the waves make.

Some can be quiet
Some can be loud
Some can whine
But this is the music the waves make.

Becky Brown (11)
Falkland St Gabriel's School

THE THINGS THAT TIME FORGOT

There are things that time forgot,
Old sunken ships with broken masts,
Or sunken cities made of marble,
How did they get there? Why?
The only things that see them now are the fish.

Who is going to dig them up?
Who is going to find them?
Who is going to marvel?
Those beautiful cities just lying there forgotten
Those things that time forgot.

Someday some people may find them,
Those sunken cities and ships,
Who can tell?
Those forgotten things of old,
The things that time forgot.

Sophie Gates (11)
Falkland St Gabriel's School

THE OLD BOOK SHOP

Creaky doors,
Broken stairs,
Silver cobwebs,
Cracking light.

Moonbeams dancing,
Torn pages curling,
Damp floorboards groaning,
Windows blocked up.

Mysterious footsteps,
Of unreal people,
Past echoes of dreamers,
Fading away.

Time telling,
Time waiting,
Till the sign on the book shop,
Reads *Open* once more.

Ailsa McCaughrean (11)
Falkland St Gabriel's School

PAST

Oh my goodness, I am going back in time.
Very fast my clock is ticking backwards
It's bringing back what's past.
Oh I remember when I stole the neighbour's cat
I wish I didn't remember.
Oh no I have gone too far.
Nothing modern in sight not even a car,
But a carriage passes me by.
Could that be Catherine Parr?
Back, back and back I go
Is that a Roman soldier do you know?
They are fighting in a field of fright
I think I need a guiding light
Could that be it . . .
I prayed to it please take me back.
I opened my eyes and there I was
Sitting upon my pink fluffy bed.

Jennie Gillam (10)
Falkland St Gabriel's School

NIGHT-TIME WANDERS

It's the middle of the night,
I'm desperate for a drink.

It seems like miles to the kitchen,
Miles to the sink.

In the bedroom next to me,
I hear a monster snore.

It's getting very loud now,
It scares me, more and more.

There's a shadow in the corner,
I wonder what is that?

On a close inspection,
I find our family cat.

Very, very gradually,
I make my way downstairs.

It's really rather gloomy,
I'm getting very scared.

I rush into the kitchen,
And reach out for the light.

Everything is normal,
There was no need to take a fright.

I pour myself some water,
And then I say . . .
Night, night.

Rebecca Thomas (10)
Falkland St Gabriel's School

JUNGLE JOURNEY

A tiger with stripes,
Hungry for food,
Searching ready for the kill,
And still I go on,
On and on.

I creep stealthily on,
Dodging in and out of trees,
Spying on any animal I see
And still I go on,
On and on.

I cantered on hungrily,
Braking cautiously now and again,
Watching every movement,
As I go,
And still I go on,
On and on.

Pacing through the jungle,
I walk in camouflage,
Over and under I go,
And still I go on,
On and on.

Buffalo charges,
A leap,
A grab,
We fall,
And still I go on,
On and on.

Hannah Harwood (11)
Falkland St Gabriel's School

SILENCE

Silence in the courtyard
Silence in the street
If you wait patiently
You will still never meet.

Silence is nothing
Nothing is a nothing
Silence is a . . . silence is a . . . silence is a nothing.

Bang, boom, bang, shh!
Listen for a silence
See, there is no such thing
Like there is no such thing as ghosts, monsters and fairy tales
Yes that's what it is, silence is a fairy tale.

Silence in the courtyard
Silence in the street
If you wait patiently
You'll never ever meet
Silence!

Sophie McCusker (10)
Falkland St Gabriel's School

THE DRAGONFLY

He flew over the swimming pool,
On a voyage it must be,
His shiny blue wings,
His body like a bee,
He took off low,
He swung up high
A dragonfly,
A dragonfly.

He flew over the hillside,
His wings flapping fast,
He was beautiful,
And wonderful,
A thing from the past,
He flew and he flew,
Very, very high,
A dragonfly,
A dragonfly,
A dragonfly.

Olivia Hudson (10)
Falkland St Gabriel's School

MALT AND ROCK JOURNEY

I've been hibernating for one hundred years,
I want to come out and play.
I can hear the children's laughter and tears,
I know that my volcano will erupt today.

My tummy begins to rumble
It's like fire, very hot
I feel the bubbles pop and tumble,
I'm going to spill my lot.

I'm slowly climbing up the wall,
To see the children play.

Woshhhhh
Boom!

'Run, run' I hear them call,
As I run down the mountain way.

Jessica Mason (10)
Falkland St Gabriel's School

LIGHTHOUSE KEEPER

Sea surrounds my stony shore,
Black waves beat at my door.
Storm winds shrieking, 'Let me in!'
The time is now, my job must begin.
I must climb the lonely stairs into the night,
There are ships out there that need my guiding light.

Foaming frenzy the ferocious sea,
Lashing at my boat, the fear overcomes me,
The north wind whistles through my hair,
What will become of the passengers in my care?
The decisions I make have to be right,
But first I need to see the guiding light.

Desperate darkness, danger and daring,
Two men alone, the lightning flaring,
One man holds the other's fate.
He must light the lamp, he mustn't be late,
Binoculars aid the captain's sight,
When will he see the guiding light?

Thunder thrashes the tearing sky,
As he struggles to climb high on high,
The captain waits, he knows it's there,
It's just a matter of when and where
The rocks are there waiting left and right,
Where is this guiding light?

Bright beams break through,
A beacon of hope, shining for captain and crew,
The keeper yawns, his long night's almost done,
The storm chased away by the morning sun,
The ship is saved at the end of the night,
As the captain sees the guiding light.

Rachel Broadbridge (11)
Falkland St Gabriel's School

THE TURTLE

In the water swims the turtle,
Gliding through the ocean wide.
On a journey through the water
Surfing on the ferocious tide.

A shell of rock for protection,
Against the dangers of the sea.
The waves splash around him, like a flame,
He just swims on, full of glee.

The wind roars around him,
An enormous lion, tearing cold everywhere,
But then under the water silence reigns,
The water world can now stop and stare!

Alice Stirmey (10)
Falkland St Gabriel's School

THE FIRE

His amber fingers,
Leap and dance,
His burning tongue,
Licks the house,
He whoops and roars.

Gripping the house,
In his flaming fingers,
He fights and conquers.

The fight is won,
The house no longer in his path,
He lingers in pride,
But carries on.

Antonia Magor (10)
Falkland St Gabriel's School

TRAVELLING THROUGH THE WOODS

I heard howls,
I saw owls,
Travelling through the woods.
I heard rats,
I saw bats,
Travelling through the woods.
I heard a fox,
I saw a box,
Travelling through the woods.
What was there?
It was hair,
Travelling through the woods.
He was dead,
He had fed,
On blood,
In the mud,
Travelling through the woods.

Hannah Gumbley (10)
Falkland St Gabriel's School

HERO

The journey of a hero,
Could be long, it could be tough,
But my hero will go on,
However short or rough.

This hero of which I'm talking,
He is a handsome prince,
But once he was a toad,
Now that made people wince.

My hero now goes onward,
He's going to take the crown,
But now there is a ditch,
So this hero must go down.

My hero is now dead,
Though I don't really mind,
For really after all,
He wasn't all that kind.

Siân Davey (10)
Falkland St Gabriel's School

TO AUSTRALIA

Yippee, today's the day,
I go to play,
Up early for a long trip,
On the plane I have to sit,
We stop off at Bangkok,
Then look at the clock,
It's still a long way,
To finish off the day,
Getting more and more excited,
To see our friends delighted,
The plane goes down with a bump,
It really made me jump,
Getting more excited making me insane,
Hooray it's time to get off the plane,
Finally through Passport Control,
It's time for our holiday to roll.

Sarah Parker (10)
Falkland St Gabriel's School

THE AEROPLANE'S VOYAGE

A voyage of
An aeroplane
Leaves behind
A long smoke trail.

It looks like
A thin line of cloud
As thin as string
As wide as a river.

Someone said
It's a
Stretched out zip
Joining up the sky.

Others say
It's the border
Between night
And day.

But to me
This voyage
Of an aeroplane
Is a long thin line
In
The
Sky.

Emma Constantine (11)
Falkland St Gabriel's School

THE HURRICANE

He travels from the sea
Quick and smooth
He hits land
And picks up a fight.

Like an earthquake
He shook the world
Distorting everything
In his path.

People are screaming
Trees are flying
He took the world apart
He ripped houses.

From the ground
He laughed and howled
Spinning and tumbling
Turning happiness to fear.

But he became tired
He was weak
And so the hurricane
Who had been so energetic
Now faded away
To peace once more.

Louise Sheridan (11)
Falkland St Gabriel's School

THE JOURNEY OF HAPPINESS

As the mountainside stood there over on the eastern side,
With one side bare,
Just a few trees stood there,
Bare of rocks,
No birds, no animals,
Just a single small wooden hut,
As lonely as an only child,
All alone, no company, no friends,
No human living there, not even a spider,
The boy of loneliness had conquered the mountainside,
But the journey had not yet begun . . .

Then one day a small child stepped out,
Beaming, smiling, laughing,
Then a mother,
They stood side by side looking around,
They danced, they played, they laughed,
And walked on the mountainside
The hut was joyful,
The mountainside was happy,
The animals came back, the plants grew,
Even the spiders,
The journey had started . . .

One day they left the mountainside,
With one side bare,
The loneliness came back,
Gripping the mountainside with his cold fingers,
The frost, licking with his icy tongue,
It was back to the mountainside with one side bare,
The people, were the people of happiness,
The journey of happiness had ended . . .

Kate Mitchell (10)
Falkland St Gabriel's School

THE CAR JOURNEY

Dog is scratching,
Baby's crying,
Child is screaming,
Mum is yelling,
Dad is humming.

Dog is barking,
Baby's still crying,
Child is arguing,
Mum is screaming,
Dad is whistling.

Dog is whining,
Baby's crying,
Child is shouting,
Mum is crying,
Dad is singing.

Dog is sleeping,
Baby's eating,
Child is complaining,
Mum is purple
Dad is laughing.

Dog is snoring,
Baby's crying,
Child is screaming,
Mum is shouting,
Dad has stopped the car.

At last they are there, at their new home.

Natasha Turner (10)
Falkland St Gabriel's School

YOU ONLY WANT A DRINK

Along the creepy hallway,
Your face is turning white,
You cannot see your fingers,
It gives you quite a fright.

You feel the wall beside you,
But cannot find the switch,
You're kind of feeling thirsty,
Your nose just starts to twitch.

But what is that before you,
A square that has four legs,
There's something else beside you,
It's only the dog that begs.

But stop, what can you hear?
Miaow, woof, woof, blub, blub,
You hear the tap is running,
Into the big blue tub.

The light comes on, you trip, you think,
You only want a drink!

Heather Handy (9)
Falkland St Gabriel's School

VOYAGE AS AN ANIMAL

A voyage to an ant could be crawling
Through grass jungles,
Just crawling over molehills,
Could be a voyage to an ant.

An adventure to a snail could be
Crawling up a gate
Just slithering up a wall,
Could be a voyage to a snail.

But for a swallow it could be swooping
Through the air,
Flying mile after mile over
Glittering oceans and winding woods.

A voyage for a wildebeest is,
Charging in thousands and thousands
Across vast grasslands and rushing rivers.
That is a voyage for a wildebeest.

Claire Nicoll (10)
Falkland St Gabriel's School

ALLITERATION JOURNEY

This is a journey from A - Z
Written in twos, just like my teacher said
So here we go . . .

Ben bit an amazing apple
Cute cuddly charming Dalmatian dogs
Exquisite elephants eat funny fat French fish
Great German gymnasts help Helen hyena
Jealous, inspired, jelly insects
Katherine kicked lovely Lucy,
My mummy meets naughty Neil
Oriana Octopus or Percy Pigeon
Racing Rachel queues quietly
Tom thinks that Samantha supports Super Sonic Slow
Vixen Vain underestimates Uranus
And . . .
Zebras zap yellow yachts.

At last that's it!

Katie Bourne (10)
Falkland St Gabriel's School

GETTING A DRINK

Bang went the
Books as I went
To get a drink.

Crash I went as
I walked into the
Door going to
Get a drink.

Creak went the
Stairs as I walked
Down them to get
A drink.

Drip went the
Tap as I turned
It on to get
A drink.

At last I said
As I got a drink.

Sophia Evans (10)
Falkland St Gabriel's School

THE LOO

I went to the loo last night and on my way there I met . . .

A massive dog with a long silver tail,
A towering robot bringing in hay by the bale.
A huge rhinoceros who was being paid,
A glittering fish women who I think was a mermaid.

By the time I got to the loo door it was morning
I knew because the sun was just dawning,
I ran back to bed as quick as a *flash*!
And ran into the door making a loud *crash*!

When I woke up there was a wet patch on the floor!

Georgina Wilson (10)
Falkland St Gabriel's School

THE JUNGLE

One day I went to the jungle to see what I could see
I met a friendly monkey who was as funny as can be.

He took me to a big old temple
It drove me a little bit mental.

I found an angry tribe
I quickly went to hide.

I ran as fast as my feet could go
My energy ran very low.

Then I bumped into a snake
He said his name was Jake.

Then I felt a little weak
And lay down in the grass to sleep.

When I woke up in my bed
My little sister said.

'Did you have a bad dream?
I heard you scream.'

Anna-Sophie Norton (10)
Falkland St Gabriel's School

TRAVELLING TO GIANT WORLD

One day I was swimming in the sea,
And a whirlpool started just by me.
I screamed and shouted help, help, help,
But all I could hear is yelp, yelp, yelp.
I started spinning round and round
And I could not hear a single sound.
Then all of a sudden whoosh . . . whoosh . . . whoosh . . .
I felt myself going with a big, big push
I saw a giant and ran for my life,
He was holding a dazzling silvery knife.
I prayed for my mother and my brother too,
But all I could say is boo hoo . . . hoo . . .
Then all of a sudden I was back on the beach,
And my mother was eating an enormous peach.

Katherine Stephens (10)
Falkland St Gabriel's School

THE BOTTOM OF A BOWLING ALLEY

The wonders of a bowling alley
Is what is at the bottom?
Is it a monster that swallows the ball?
And spits it out again
Or is it a ghost that just brings it back
I'll never know if there is a
Vicious monster down there
I will throw the ball and wait for the sound,
Is that horrendous sound a good sign or a bad sign?
The bottom of a bowling alley will always be
A mystery to me!

Harriet Drury (10)
Falkland St Gabriel's School

I WILL RUN AWAY FROM HOME!

I will run away from home,
I will if you're not nice to me,
Then I will run away from home,
I'll hide behind a tree maybe.

I'll run away to sea one day,
I'll vanish without a trace,
I'll run away to sea one day,
And I will have a big, smiley face.

I will run away from school,
Do no maths, or English at all,
I will run away from school,
Don't worry I'll be sure to call.

Bethany Hensman (10)
Falkland St Gabriel's School

A TRIP TO SCHOOL

I jumped out of bed and
Heard a creepy noise, I jumped
On the bus just in time
To get to the tide.
I got an ice cream and
Swam in the sea.
Then I went on the trampoline
I walked to the station and
Jumped on the train
I got to school just
Too late and that's
What I do day
After day.

Rebecca Povey (9)
Falkland St Gabriel's School

JOURNEY THROUGH YOSEMITE NATIONAL PARK, CALIFORNIA

As I was going along
A long dusty path
I saw a small snake
That quickly slithered past
It had black and yellow scaly skin
He disappeared under a giant redwood tree.

I saw a tiny chipmunk
Quickly scampering past
Black and white stripes
All across him
Then he quickly ran
Scrambling up a big squoia tree.

A big black hungry bear
Coming towards me
From the big lake
I thought he looked hungry
Looking at his teeth
So I ran and left him very hungry.

A huge mountain lion
Creeping out from a big rock
I'm crouching down behind a bush
Not moving a muscle
There is a big waterfall
Water dropping into a lake.

Rosaleen Morshead (9)
Falkland St Gabriel's School

EXIST, NOT EXTINCT

The sun's going down, all is quiet.
Ripples dance on the water as though they were clowns
The sun glistens down on the exposed pool,
As faded umbrellas tilt their heads towards the water cool
The black notes of a melody enticing in the air
Dusk approaches as a ball of fire,
As rabbits hop beneath restrictive wire
This is autumn!

Swallows skim along the waters surface to catch an insect
Is their purpose
Where they may go or where they may be is a great secret
To you and to me
They congregate on rooftops, like gossips in a coffee shop
They swerve and glide their friend with wind blowing them alongside.
The woods wave and the stars say goodnight
Storm despises them and cuts off their race of flight.
But they keep going at the speed of light
South welcomes them with open arms, warm and bright.

I follow her; she beams at me in her silver gown.
My song echoes into the night and pleases her
She howls at me for her every whim
Through every one of the seven seas, she is by my side
I hear my herd singing like the wind beckoning me to come
'Please wait' I mourned 'Don't go south without me'
The moon cries nothing but soft languid tones
I won't remain forever - for I am the whale.

Alice French (11)
Falkland St Gabriel's School

THE CHAOTIC AEROPLANE TRIP

I'm getting ready to go on the aeroplane to Singapore,
On a holiday, it's going to be great I'm sure.
We get on the aeroplane and off we go,
Higher and higher in the flow.
I can hear so many noises like . . .
Dads snoring,
Kids shouting,
Mums stressed out,
Toddlers running about,
Babies crying,
I wish I could get there, fast, in a tick,
I'm starting to feel like I need the toilet quick.
The aisles blocked, oh what a muddle,
Could someone help me through before I make a puddle.
I get there in the end and go back to my seat,
Are we nearly there? I'll die if I don't eat.
Half an hour to go, I think I'll have a sleep
I then wake up and we're there,
We get our bags and off we get
I'll never forget that aeroplane trip,
I've never known a place so chaotic!
But oh dear me I've just remembered,
I've got to go back at the end of September!

Olivia Watson (10)
Falkland St Gabriel's School

THUNDER IN THE MOONLIGHT

I was travelling through the thunder
In a thick, black forest.

The lightning lit the sky
With a flash that caught my eye.

The rain went pitter-patter on the trees
The wind went whoosh and scattered leaves.

I heard a thud
And saw some blood, but didn't know what to do.

Alicia Beavon (10)
Falkland St Gabriel's School

THE SCHOOL TRIP

I'm going on a school trip
I'm going to the zoo
I'm getting on a coach
And Sally's coming too.

We driving down the roadway
We're going through the gate
'Hurry up, get in line
We don't want to be late.'

First, we visit the rhino
Then we look at the bear
The lion really scares us
The wolf lives in a lair.

We're getting really hungry
It's nearly time for lunch
We go to see the monkeys
They seem a happy bunch.

It's time to go back to school
It's been a smashing day
Our mums will be waiting
Three cheers, hip, hip, hooray!

Helen Brandwood (10)
Falkland St Gabriel's School

THE OLD TO THE NEW

I am an American visiting England for a year. These are my thoughts.

The Mayflower brought the Pilgrims
My mommy brought me
What should I bring to this old world I see?

Peanut butter, fluff, all that stuff
Jelly in my belly, all that stuff
So I go from the tea party
To the London Zoo
I went home on the Mayflower
My mommy brought me too.
Look what I bring to this new world I see.

Victoria Mueck (10)
Falkland St Gabriel's School

A POEM TO MAKE YOU THINK ABOUT POLLUTION

Pollution is a bad thing, I know
Oil spills kill birds on the shore
Left-over rubbish spoils their home
Litter which should have gone home.
Unclean water poisons us all
Then the poison goes up the food chain
In the end poisoning us
Only because we did not take care
Now is the time to act, before it's too late!

Katie Stainthorp (8)
Falkland St Gabriel's School

POLLUTION

If the world was not polluted
How happy we would be
No cars, factories or aeroplanes
No burning down the trees.

No chimneys upon our houses
No petrol tanks on cars
If only we could walk to school
If only it wasn't that far.

If our transport ran on controls
A better world we'd live on
Don't you think it would be better
If pollution was gone?

Chelsie Paul (9)
Falkland St Gabriel's School

OUR EARTH

Think what we could do to help our Earth,
Do you think it is as good as it was at birth?
Think what you could do to make our world better,
Stop cruelty to life; trees coming down and litter
If only our thoughtlessness never had to start,
Could you help cruelty be a thing of the past?
So help make our Earth a better place,
And not let it be in such a big state.

Helen Broadbridge (8)
Falkland St Gabriel's School

Journey To The Nowhere Part Of France

We could have gone to Italy or gone to see a dance
But of all the things we could have done we had to go to France
Oh what a journey it was such a real bore
It seemed like a decade, perhaps even more!

It turned out we were staying in a nowhere part of France
No cinema, no supermarket not even some place to dance
To get to the shops it took a long while
We certainly travelled for more than a mile.

I felt like eating so I tried cottage pie
It made me sick and I started to cry
Then I got better and decided to ride
On a bike far too big for me 'Stop, Dad' I cried.

In that same week an accident occurred
Oh dear, a Concorde on fire or so we had heard
We travelled around with so much to see
Roman pavilions, baths and stops for tea.

All in all the holiday was a disaster
Be sure to bring more than a plaster
How about same time next year?
I hardly think so my dear.

Sarah Duggan (10)
Falkland St Gabriel's School

Make This World Better

In the streets of London
There was oil all around.

All is most horrible all around
Could we make our future better now?

Why, why is this so horrible?
Why does it have to be now?

I hate this world it's changed so much.

It can't happen now, it just can't happen now.

Josephine Thorp-Olesen (8)
Falkland St Gabriel's School

SNOW

Tossing, turning,
Straggling, stirring.

Lie still on the ground
Wait till morning when she'll be found.

Still, steady,
Flopping, dropping.

Lie waiting till sunlight was bound
Hearing anything that went on even the greyhound.

Swirling, whirling,
Till she'll be found.

Sunlight shone
And woke up everyone.

Shining, ironing,
Blinding, finding.

Melting her into water
Finally he had caught her.

Natasha Westbrook (11)
Falkland St Gabriel's School

HOLIDAY

We're going on holiday today
Everyone's rushing around
Dad packs the last suitcase
While we jump into the car.

Soon we're at the airport
Having our passports checked
I'm getting really excited
I hope we're going soon.

Now we are on the aeroplane
It has just taken off
I'm looking out of the window
Everything looks small.

My sister says she can see Africa
I say she can't
We're getting really close now
I can't wait 'til we land.

We've landed now and we're walking off
It's very sunny outside
I'm really going to enjoy this holiday
I can't wait to go and swim.

Kirsten Riddick (9)
Falkland St Gabriel's School

OUR WORLD

When will the world learn?
Will animals still be alive?
Please let the world learn.

I hope the world will learn,
It really does annoy me.
Sometimes I think will the world
Still be the same when I grow up?

Rachel Bristow (8)
Falkland St Gabriel's School

A VOYAGE OF BLACK BEAUTY

Her sails they billowed in the breeze,
She sailed across the calming seas.
All we sailed the crew and me,
She was the great Black Beauty.

The captain yelled 'Ahoy, me men'.
He sneaked inside his gloomy den.
We left behind the yellow sands,
And sailed away to far-off lands.

The clouds rolled in, the sky grew grey,
To bring upon an awful day.
The ship it rocked and rocked and rolled,
The night was fierce and very cold.

The ship it swayed us all to sleep,
As we sailed through the ocean deep.
We slept so soundly without a yawn
To get up early at the dawn.

We woke to find a welcoming shore,
We had to live alone no more.
At last the end was very near,
Now we had no more storms to fear.

Bronwen Edwards (11)
Falkland St Gabriel's School

WHAT WILL LIFE BE LIKE WHEN I GROW UP?

When I grow up will anything be healthy?
Will there be clean water?
Will there be any animals left?

When I grow up will anything live?
Will you have left me anything?
Will wild plants grow?

When I grow up will anything be happy?
Will the Earth have peace?
Will it have any goodness left?

Please leave me something.

Charlotte Garner (8)
Falkland St Gabriel's School

NOVEMBER THE 5TH

The bonfire hissed like
A load of snakes hissing
And the fireworks exploded
Like a bomb
The colours sprinkled all
Over the sky
The Catherine wheels went
Round and round
Sparks came out like
Twirling stars
A screamer went off
With a
Bang!

Becky Westall (8)
Falkland St Gabriel's School

VOYAGES

Grab your coats,
Grab your bags,
We're going on a voyage.

We're going to sail the seven seas,
We're going on a voyage.
We're gong to see the seven wonders of the world,
We're going on a voyage.

We're going to the ocean's depth,
We're going on a voyage.
We're going to go to Jupiter,
We're going on a voyage.

We're going to the Sahara Desert,
We're going on a voyage.
We're going to the Arctic,
We're going on a voyage.

We're going to bed,
We're going on a dream voyage.

Maddy Debney (11)
Falkland St Gabriel's School

NOVEMBER THE 5TH

Beautiful fireworks
Crackling in the sky
Bonfires burning
Fantastic Catherine wheels
Spinning round and round
Rockets exploding in the sky
Sparklers sparkling so bright.

Polly London (8)
Falkland St Gabriel's School

THE TIME CAPSULE

I stepped into my room
Held my breath to see
A multicoloured blur
Swirling out at me.

A whirling mist
The speed of time
Through this capsule
The journey's mine.

A gallant joust
A flash of steel
Knights in armour
It feels so real.

I'm back in time.

Olivia Hills (10)
Falkland St Gabriel's School

FIREWORKS

November the 5th
The day for fireworks!
Catherine wheels and
Rockets too.
Beautiful bright bonfires,
Sparkling sparklers,
Frizzling and flickering fireworks
I absolutely love it!

Katie Handley Potts (8)
Falkland St Gabriel's School

A TRIP TO FLORIDA

We're on our way to Florida
We're driving in the car
We're going to the airport,
It isn't very far.

We're now inside the airport
We're queuing with our bags
Dad's talking to a lady
Who's putting on our tags.

We're getting on the plane now
It's very posh inside
The seats are very comfy
And very, very wide.

The flight is very bumpy
The clouds are very thick
The passenger beside me
Is looking rather sick.

The plane is coming in to land
My seat belt's very tight
The earth is moving very fast
The sun is very bright.

We're in Orlando Airport now
We're looking for a car
Dad's hoping for a limousine
Which has a mini-bar.

At last we are on holiday
In the Florida sun
We're going to visit Disney World
And have a lot of fun.

Charlotte Keast (10)
Falkland St Gabriel's School

I Think I'm Seeing Things From Space!

As I shoot through the stars,
Looking out for comets,
Some debris whizzing past my ear,
Knocks me off course.
I land on Mars,
Instead of Jupiter,
Then out pop twenty little Martians,
Am I seeing thing or is this real?
Are there really Martians at my feet?
Suddenly a cosmic wind scoops me off my feet.
My journey's done,
I'm heading home,
With a Martian at my heel!

Sophie Totten (9)
Falkland St Gabriel's School

The Day Has Arrived

Come, come
To the fireworks display
There's going to be fantastic fireworks
That frizzle in the sky
Beautiful, colourful fireworks
Exploding everywhere
Come, come
And have fun.

Francesca Robertson (8)
Falkland St Gabriel's School

GETTING TO SCHOOL

Alarm goes,
Wake up,
Get changed,
Eat breakfast,
Brush teeth,
Grab bag,
Rush out,
Catch bus,
Stop at school,
Get off,
Bell goes.

Made it!

Chantelle Rizan (9)
Falkland St Gabriel's School

FIREWORKS NIGHT

Terrific fireworks exploding loudly
Shooting up like hissing stars
Shouts and laughing from cheerful mothers
Colourful, frizzling, popping fireworks
Whizzing and fizzing through the air
Catherine wheels turning
Then it all dies down and people pack up
And drive home.

Olivia McBain Morrish (8)
Falkland St Gabriel's School

THE YEAR'S VOYAGE

Freezing and dark,
Wet and tired,
Dead trees and plants,
The end of the year,
Winter gets depressing.

Then! . . .

Fresh and dry,
Wild and happy,
New plants,
New life,
Spring is exciting.

Suddenly! . . .

Warm and light,
Clean and bright,
The same plants
The same life,
I like summer.

Wait! . . .

Tough and clean,
Cold and crispy,
Crunching leaves,
Falling from trees,
I love autumn.

Soon enough!

Freezing and dark,
Wet and tired,

Dead trees and plants,
The end of the year,
Winter comes too soon.

But there's still next year.

Oriana Williams (10)
Falkland St Gabriel's School

THE BOAT TRIP TO FRANCE

We are on the boat,
We have left the land,
It has been chaos since we pushed off from the sand!

People are crying,
They want their mums,
But I am just casual, I don't look glum!

Teachers cannot cope,
We are two hours away,
It will take at least 'til the end of the day!

Not a sign of France,
I think we are lost,
I think we are going to pay the cost!

We are nearly there,
I think I see France
I am so happy I will do a dance!

We are here at last,
In Calais,
And finally it is the end of the day.

Lucy Peacock (9)
Falkland St Gabriel's School

THE HORSE

Galloping through the woods,
Hearing nothing but the beat of its hooves,
And the gentle drip, drip, drip of the rain,
Galloping faster, faster and faster,
Running away from man,
It slows into a canter,
Then a trot,
Trotting through the stream,
Its black eyes shining and coat gleaming
Camouflaged with the black night,
It turns away and gallops,
Gallops, gallops on into the night.

Becky Hunter (11)
Falkland St Gabriel's School

NOVEMBER THE 5TH

Fantastic, flickering fireworks
Glistening in the sky,
Wonderful, crackling, hissing bonfires
Like bombs.
One thousand frizzling sparks
In the dark night air
Catherine wheels spinning
Fast as wheels on cars
Cheerful, crackling, flying rockets
Like aeroplanes starting.

Harriet Riddick (8)
Falkland St Gabriel's School

A DARK VOYAGE TO THE KITCHEN

A loud snort like a fiery dragon
Just Dad.

Creaking floorboards
Like a spooky house
When the door crashes open
Tripping over something
Big and hairy
A tremendous groan
Just the dog.

Yellow eyes floating in the darkness
Just the cat.

A shout 'No don't do it - it's mine'
Just Jake sleep talking again.

Slipping down the stair
A lurch in my stomach
Carefully opening the door
A shadow on the wall
Just the table.

An eerie green glow
Just the fish tank.

Flicking on the light switch
It's just the kitchen.

Ellie May Holland (10)
Falkland St Gabriel's School

ON THE WAY TO SPACE

Floating around
On the way to space.
It feels like flying
On the way to space.

Stars are everywhere
On the way to space.
With a few planets
On the way to space.

We will see the moon
On the way to space.
And Venus and Mars
On the way to space.

We will collect some moon dust
When we're in space.
And meet some aliens
When we're in space.

We will tell all our stories
When we get back from space.
And say hello to gravity
When we get back from space.

Charlotte Weeks (9)
Falkland St Gabriel's School

SHIPPING

As she drifts from the breezy shore,
The crew are waving more and more.

The sun going down above their heads,
As they make their way slowly to their beds.

The splash of water at the crack of dawn,
Wakes the crew to a sunny morn.

The shore they left so long ago,
Leaving in the past their friends and foe.

As they near the end of their sunny cruise,
The weather changes suddenly full of disaster and abuse.

The boat's gentle sway turns into a mighty rock,
As hopes faded of reaching the ending dock.

Eleanor Johnston (11)
Falkland St Gabriel's School

My Childhood

When I was a baby in mum's arms,
I looked at her with all my charms,
When I was small and laid in my cot
I dreamed of when I would be a tot,
When I crawled across the floor,
I trapped my fingers in the door,
Time quickly flew passed.
I'm a toddler at last,
I toddled up the garden path
While mum and dad stood and laughed,
Now I've reached the age of three
I nearly know my ABC.
I went to nursery when I was four
I got locked behind the toilet door,
When I was the age of six
I went to the circus where they did lots of funky tricks,
When I was eight I was in quite a state
When I broke my mum's best plate.
I joined St Gabriel's School when I was nine
And I have had a fantastic time,
Now that I am ten this is the end of my childhood journey.

Kerry Gerdes-Hansen (10)
Falkland St Gabriel's School

DIVING

Dived . . .
Yes I dived
Deep under the sea
It felt so wonderful
I was free
Gliding into a void
Not knowing what would happen to me.

Fish weaving through my hair
I stop for a minute and stare.

I am on a voyage
My voyage
To find the answer of my prayer.

Imogen Collins (11)
Falkland St Gabriel's School

THE UNWANTED JOURNEY

Bounding through the grass
Antlers in the air
Running away from a tiger
It was pouncing and snarling
We leapt past four long legs
It was hot and dry
We paused for a drink
The air smelt different
We were a long way from home.

Joanne Madeley (10)
Falkland St Gabriel's School

THE SCHOOL TRIP

Lining up at the classroom door
Waiting for the bus to arrive
Children start playing the fool
While the teacher is watching the clock.

The bus arrives at ten o'clock
Chattering children start clambering on
The busman drives as slow as a tortoise
The children sing out of tune songs as the scenery whizzes by.

The bus arrives at twelve o'clock
Now the fun begins
There is Tyrannosaurus Rex and Brontosaurus
Dinosaur's eggs of all shapes and sizes
Skeletons as big as double-decker buses
The children busily started to write.

It's lunchtime
Out comes the ham and cheese sandwiches
Crisps and chocolate bars
And cans of fizzy drink
Now it's time to go home.

The class climbs on the bus
Talking about the wonderful things they have seen
Huge monsters of a long time ago
A day the class will always remember.

Leah Vellam-Steptoe (10)
Falkland St Gabriel's School

THE SCHOOL TRIP

We're going to the zoo
Me, my class, my teacher too
We might see a lion
Maybe a bear
Who knows until we are there.

Hooray, hooray we're here, we're here
Look at the birds and parrots
One has a multicoloured tail
It looks fine
'Come on children keep in line'
Say the teachers from behind.

'Jane 'Yes', Peter 'Yes', Ben . . .'
'Over here in the lion's den!'
Roar went the lion getting closer to Ben
'What are you doing in there?
That doesn't matter
Now just get out then.'
Phew!
Now I am safe at school again.

Nicola Bates (9)
Falkland St Gabriel's School

TRAVELLING

You walk for miles until you feel unenergetic
You travel in a car that makes you feel sick.

And travel on that boring plane,
You sit about with nothing to gain.

And there are those long journeys
On a boat that moves at ease.

And of course there is that train,
When all the passengers complain.

But those rockets, they are fun,
They rush up towards the sun.

Myriam Frenkel (10)
Falkland St Gabriel's School

VOYAGE

I should like to stand and go,
Where the leafy palm trees grow,
Where God looks upon us in the skies
In the seas where anchors lie,
And where a North Asian stands and hums,
Where an Australian bangs on his drums,
Where when you swim along the Nile
And come face to face with a crocodile,
Where you go to sleep at night,
And wake to find no morning light,
Where a pig puts on wings and flies,
Where you see kindness in a tiger's eyes,
Where you stand in an empty house,
And hear nothing but a tiny mouse,
Where you turn a corner and find the toys
Of all the old Egyptian boys,
Then seeing Pop Stars sitting in the gloom
Then sleeping in the dining room,
I'd like to see where Santa goes
Where trees and leaves and seeds all blow,
I'd love to go all around the world
And see the wonders that it holds.

Lara Woodhead (11)
Falkland St Gabriel's School

It's Funny Walking To School

I was walking to school one day,
When suddenly I saw,
A light in the pathway.

At first I felt quite frightened,
And then very afraid,
I kept on walking on and on.

Until I found out why,
This light in the pathway,
Was kind of like a spy!

I knew it was from the future,
Or maybe from the past,
It's funny walking to school.

I thought of the things,
I could do,
If I walked inside the light.

I could go to ancient Egypt,
See the pyramids
And tombs!

I could go to the future,
See all the new things,
To begin!

But I decided not to,
To go straight off to school,
It's funny walking to school!

Sophie Hunter (9)
Falkland St Gabriel's School

MY VOYAGE

In the middle of the night
I walked across the hall,
I tripped, but the carpet broke my fall,
Oh how it hurt, I even ripped my dad's best shirt.

I slithered into bed
And as I was laying down my head
Someone came in my room,
There was a loud crash then a boom.

In the morning my alarm woke me up
Then my brother came in
'What are you doing?' I said
You're nearly half-dead.

It was a hard voyage,
Getting out of my bed,
I could feel the dizziness in my head
I could you know.

I had to go to school,
And do swimming in the pool.
A big person gave me a punch
All because I wouldn't give him my lunch.

Finally school was over,
I rushed home to get some food,
But when I got there
I wasn't in the mood.

Now back to the evening my next voyage
Will happen tomorrow and it will bring me back to sorrow . . . school!

Cara Jewell (11)
Falkland St Gabriel's School

DEATH

An old man weeps,
It creeps . . .
A lady cries,
It slides . . .
A child screams,
It gleams . . .
What is it?
It's . . .

A climber falls,
It crawls . . .
A hiker hurts,
It blurts . . .
'Oh Joy!'
What could it be?
It's . . .

I know you know
What it is!
Out of your pain,
It gets bliss!

It wanders the earth,
Waiting for birth,
To take at the end of the line!

It tortures you until the end,
So you ask
What is it?

It's . . .
Well you'll find out,
Soon enough!

Chantelle Davison (11)
Falkland St Gabriel's School

OVER THE HILLS

Over the hills where the bluebells grow
Over the hills where the poppies blow
Over the hills there's a way we know
Down to a whispering wood.

Over the hills where the mushrooms grow
Over the hills where the pansies blow
Over the hills there's a way we know
Down to a rippling brook.

Over the hills where the daisies grow
Over the hills where the breezes blow
Over the hills where there's a way we know
Down to a freshening field.

Over the hills where the flowers grow
Over the hills where the trees blow
Over the hills there's a way we know
Up to a steeply sloped cliff.

Over the hills where the rainbows go
Where coloured shrubs and brambles grow
Over the hills there's a way we know
Down to a rolling sea.

Natalie Hyde (11)
Falkland St Gabriel's School

THE VOYAGE

I will take you on a voyage,
Travelling far and wide,
I will take you on this voyage,
To distant lands, never seen before.

I will take you deep in the jungle,
Where ancient cities lay buried,
I will take you to the top of the mountains,
Where you can touch the sky.

I will take you through the desert,
Where the Sphinx will pose his riddle,
I will take you to the depths of the ocean,
Where mermaids will show you the way.

I will take you on a voyage
If only you believe
I will take you on this voyage
The voyage of your mind.

Clarisse Loughrey (10)
Falkland St Gabriel's School

THE MOON

T he moon in the sky is bright
H e wakes up at night
E veryone gazes up at his face.

M any spaceships join the race
O ne man has bought a piece of the moon
O ne man hopes to holiday soon
N obody knows that I would like to go too.

Sophie Raine (9)
Falkland St Gabriel's School

THE FUTURE

The future what will it hold for me?
Probably an ice cream as big as can be.
The moon is round like a big apple pie
But the people! Oh my!
They're all robots, what a surprise
What if there was no gravity there?
We would all be floating in the air
The future, what is in store for me?
I will just have to wait and see.

Georgina Freestone (9)
Falkland St Gabriel's School

THE RIVER

Springs bubbling like the bubbles from the tank of a scuba diver
Streams greeting each other like old friends at a confluence point
Whirlpools whizzing fish around
Waves coming again and again like thunder
The water is his clear skin
He drops his flesh to create the delta
The salt comes from his chips
He slides down again and again to create waterfalls
He's wet. Everlasting
He slides along pebbles like a jet ski
The meander is his smile
At the end he drops his load
And he floats into the sea
Yet another day will dawn for him
A new life.

Nicholas Payne (9)
Finchampstead CE Primary School

WEATHER

What is the sun?
A big yellow circle as big as the world
It is red-hot - hotter than a light bulb
That has been on for ages.

What is a cloud?
They are like big fluffy rabbits.

What is thunder?
A big loud bang of a bomb exploding.

What is rain?
A bucket of water coming from the sky.

Becky Williams (9)
Finchampstead CE Primary School

WEATHER

What is hail?
The weather showing how cold it is.

When does the sun shine?
When time for happiness has started.

Why do raindrops fall?
Because God has left the tap on.

What is snow?
Crystal raindrops flowing like a river.

Melissa Howe (9)
Finchampstead CE Primary School

WHAT IS WEATHER?

What is rain?
It rains because clouds are eating onions
And their eyes are watering.

What is snow?
When God is eating ice cream
And drops lots of it.

When does lightning strike?
When God gets angry.

What is hail?
When ice cubes drop from
Outer space.

Ben Hopkinson (9)
Finchampstead CE Primary School

WEATHER

What is thunder?
The black Devil's gold fillings hurled into the sky.

What is snow?
Fluffy cotton wool swiftly falling.

What is rain?
The end to poor people's lives.

What is the sun?
The black Devil holding up his menacing eye.

Harvey Coles (10)
Finchampstead CE Primary School

WHAT IS WEATHER?

What is thunder?
God roaring when he's mad.

When does rain come?
When God cries tears of happiness.

What's the sun?
The burning breath of a dragon.

What is a rainbow?
A happy, kind, smile.

What is snow?
God spraying creamy icing on the Earth.

What is lightning?
A supersonic flash of electricity.

What are hailstones?
Crystal rocks that shimmer in the light.

Emma Osler (9)
Finchampstead CE Primary School

WEATHER

What is rain?
The clouds tears of laughter when they tickle each other.

How does snow come?
When the clouds drop crumbs all over the Earth.

What is the wind?
It is when Hell opened his wings.

Sam Paulden (9)
Finchampstead CE Primary School

THE RIVER

The source begins his journey, ready to reach his destination
The sea!
Streams, meeting and greeting old friends
As they reach the confluence point
Rapids whooshing as fast as possible taking everything he needs
with him
Whirlpool, he's angry and annoyed, spinning around
Making everything in his clasp dizzy
The waterfall, her happiness and joy make a great slide for playful fish
Meander, he whooshes around the corners to the end of the racetrack.
At the delta he drops his load, exhausted from his tiring journey
At the estuary, he reaches the sea
Slowly he flows peacefully into the sea
Ready to make a new life.

Amy Gray (11)
Finchampstead CE Primary School

THE RIVER

A spring bubbling up as a warm welcome to everyone
Rapids whooshing like people on a rollercoaster
Streams greeting family at a confluence point
Swerving around the meander like Michael Schumacher
He drops down waterfalls like daring bungee jumpers
Pebbles playing hide and seek amongst the water reeds
He zooms off again, gaining on the sea
He slows down and relaxes
He drops his load
And the estuary opens his huge mouth so he can flow through
And meet his old friends.

Elizabeth Merritt (10)
Finchampstead CE Primary School

WEATHER

What is snow?
Tiny crystals falling to the ground.

What is wind?
God's mighty breath as he watches the Earth.

What are stars?
Sparks from fireworks that got stuck in the sky.

What is a rainbow?
Angels showing the world God keeps his promises.

What is the sun?
The light of Heaven.

Vicky Briggs (9)
Finchampstead CE Primary School

WEATHER

Why does it snow?
Because God's heater broke.

Why does it rain?
Because God went in a freezing salty shower.

Why does hail fall?
Because everyone in Heaven is playing golf.

What is lightning?
It is God getting angry because
Some ungrateful soul is calling
Rude names on Earth.

Bradley Watmore (9)
Finchampstead CE Primary School

ICE

Why does ice fall?
Because God freezes over and falls into pieces.

How is ice made?
Crystals which shiver and fall down to Earth.

When do you see ice?
When the glass crystals frost as quick
As a cheetah and then falls down from the sky.

Who controls ice?
The unfriendly, chilly, icy Queen of Ice.

What is ice like?
A forbidding, frost-bound glaze across the world.

Why does ice fall?
Because God freezes over and falls into pieces.

Rachna Joshi (10)
Finchampstead CE Primary School

THE RIVER

He bubbles up like a shaken bottle of soda
He jumps off waterfalls thinking he's a child
He swings little fish around, angrily
Making them feel sick
He races around meanders like he's in a police car
Pebbles hide from his presence, behind the weed
He races over rapids, thinking he's a bird
He slows down and drops his load
As if he's finished a day at the mall.

Mathew Watmore (11)
Finchampstead CE Primary School

THE RIVER

Shallow river, getting ready for a journey of life
Waterfalls whooshing down like people quickly driving to work
Meanders swirling around corners as fast as a person on an
obstacle course.
Estuary's in traffic greeting good friends
He dodges through the rapids
The reflection from the sun is his shining teeth
He makes me want to go with the flow,
He slows down trying to form a delta feeling very tired
He relaxes and drifts off to the sea meeting
New friends like a new beginning.

Sophie Barrow (10)
Finchampstead CE Primary School

THIS IS A TALE OF A BOY CALLED BABBIT

This is a tale of a boy called Babbit
Who had a really disgusting habit,
Of picking his nose and biting his toes,
And doing this wherever he goes,
One day his windpipe did get blocked,
And his mum said he ought to have stopped,
Then a fly went up his nose,
And he got into a sneezing pose,
Then his lips started to part,
And out came his brain, liver and heart,
Then a shout came 'My son he's dead',
And there he lay in his bloodstained bed.

Alex Gillett (9)
Finchampstead CE Primary School

BEST THINGS

Hot steaming chips,
Pulling on football kits,
Maths and science,
Experiments,
Weekends,
Holidays on end,
Cubs,
Meeting friendly buds,
Canute House tomorrow,
Seeing a rabbit near its burrow,
Pets,
Playing football near the wrecks,
Computer fun,
Eating a chocolate bun,
That's enough for today
Can you come round to play?

Philip Saville (8)
Finchampstead CE Primary School

THE RIVER

There she goes, speeding through a race
She pushes water off the edge of a waterfall
She chases water which makes rapids
She breathes coldness into the water
Her pets are cute fish
Her fresh water dates the salt water of the estuary
At the end of the day she is so tired
She sits down on the delta.

Michelle Robinson (10)
Finchampstead CE Primary School

BEST THINGS

Sweets from the cupboard
And toys from the shop
And even vegetables I like to chop.

The smell of winter's day and
I'm paddling all day.
Apple juice and shopping
Bike riding to friends and TV
A sister too.
Chips and chocolate
And McDonald's too.
Computer and bed and lots more too.
I think that's enough for one day or two
I will be back quite soon.

Cressida Harris (8)
Finchampstead CE Primary School

THE RIVER

Her source whooshes like children at the start of a race
Her streams greeting each other like old friends at the confluence point
She throws the fish away like a roundabout bouncing people off
She jumps off the waterfall as if it was a diving board
She's rushing through the rapids like nothing is there
She runs around the meander eager to win
She drops her load at the delta like a tired shopper
Now she's all tired, drifting sleepily to the sea
Meeting with her new friends.

Simon Annan (11)
Finchampstead CE Primary School

BEST THINGS

Snow to throw, chips to eat,
socks to wear upon my feet.

Lollies to lick, apples to bite,
toys to cuddle in the night!

Teachers to teach us, friends to hug,
warming chocolate from my mug!

Going to bed, summer sun,
going out and having fun!

Balls to play with, sweets to chew,
friends to play with me and you!

Danielle Wakefield-Piggott (9)
Finchampstead CE Primary School

WOOD-EATING GUS

This is the tale of a boy named Gus
Whose eating habit caused a fuss.
His favourite hobby was eating wood
He even hid it in his hood.
He pulled it off the jungle tree
To eat when he was home with me
He put it up his nose one day
And then he sadly passed away.

Robert Row (8)
Finchampstead CE Primary School

BEST THINGS

An exciting football match,
Soft things in a patch,
Playing on my Game Boy,
Shopping for a toy,
Sweets and pets,
Typically not to the vets,
Friends around,
£1.00 pocket money,
School holiday.
When you're going away,
Some smells,
Playing with bells
Cubs,
The school seat belonging to H R Bud,
Maths,
But some people can be really daft,
Bikes,
On really long hikes,
Electronic fun,
A tasty bun,
And more,
But I am starting to bore.

Thomas Kennington (8)
Finchampstead CE Primary School

HORNBY TRAIN SETS

My favourite thing will be,
A train set by Hornby.
I have a Hornby one,
It gives me so much fun.

I have some carriages,
For people in and out.
I like to drive the train,
And direct the route.

Jonathan Ellenby (8)
Finchampstead CE Primary School

BEST THINGS!

I like shopping for clothes of course,
I like watching Doctor Morse!
I like swimming in a pool,
Don't you think it's really cool?

I like jumping up and down
I like thinking I'm a clown
I like flying in the air
I like cuddling my teddy bear!

I like watching my TV
I like singing Ce La Vie!
I like cooking with my mum
I like eating hot cross buns!

I like snuggling in my bed,
I like cuddling with my ted,
If I go on any more,
I'm afraid I'll start to bore!

So now it's time to say farewell,
So let's hope, you'll stay quite well!

Hayley Wilson (9)
Finchampstead CE Primary School

RAIN

Raindrops falling, falling from the sky
Like tearful clouds why, oh why?
The birds in the trees calling out
A hypnotic song pouring out
Fox cubs running, running to their mother
Why do animals love the summer?
The clouds gather, gather round
A flash of light a rumbling sound
Of God, shouting, shouting down
All gather round and come and see
The beauties of the world, made by me.

Niomi O'Rourke (9)
Finchampstead CE Primary School

THINGS I LIKE

I like squishy peas
Softening the batter on my fish.
I like milky chocolate
Melting over my tongue.
I like salty chips
When they're soft and plump.
I like my pets
When my fish goes gurgle! Gurgle! Gurgle!

William Malins (9)
Finchampstead CE Primary School

WEATHER

What is sun?
It's a big ball that's gleaming orange.

What is lightning?
It's God throwing spears down from Heaven.

What is snow?
It's bits of ice cream falling from God.

What is the moon?
It's slices of sleepy cheese floating in the sky.

Lewis Gallagher (7)
Finchampstead CE Primary School

MY ICE FLAKE POEM

I   ce flakes twinkling in the air,
C   old frosty shimmering stars,
E   ach day I wake up to see.

F   lakes on my seat outside,
L   akes
A   re covered in shimmering snowflakes,
K   atherine's watching as . . .
E   very snowflake gliding down.

Katherine Lawrence (8)
Finchampstead CE Primary School

THINGS I LIKE

I like breakfast, dinner and tea,
And I like to eat on my knee.
I like hearing lovely things,
And I like almost anything.

I like my mum and dad,
Because they are so mad.
I sometimes like school,
Because sometimes cool.

My brother's a pain,
Just when it rains.

I have to say
I like the USA.

My dad doesn't wear a tie,
I just can't understand why.

My dad is moaning,
I have to stop phoning.

I have to say goodbye,
Otherwise I have to pie.
I like breakfast, dinner and tea,
But best of all I like *me*!

Marlene Maree (9)
Finchampstead CE Primary School

SUNSHINE!

S ome people say they hate the sun but I
U se the sun to see places,
N ever say you hate the sun,
S am is my best friend and
H e says he likes the sun
I agree with him the sun is very brill so
N ever say you hate the sun or
E verybody will think you are a fool!

Julia Bedser (8)
Finchampstead CE Primary School

ANIMALS

Soft furry burning paws,
Sleekly shiny hard shell,
Large spiky brown bears,
Small big pink ears,
Large slobbery teeth,
Red-hot wild eyes,
Fast monstrous ugly rhinoceros,
Yellow and brown long necks,
Little cuddle soft ears,
Green scale lumpy skin,
And all the other animals.

Danniella O'Sullivan (9)
Francis Baily Primary School

SQUIRRELS

Squirrels flash from tree to tree to meet their friends at the other side
The squirrels have bushy tails and they go from side to side
The squirrels are small when they are babies
When they're adult they are big.
There are happy squirrels all day long
There are fluffy squirrels and friends like pelicans
They run fast like pelicans
They're tall and short
There are lots of squirrels in the land
The squirrels are getting more popular.

Anna Beckett (8)
Francis Baily Primary School

DRAGONS

The red-hot flames charge out of his mouth
Fire-breathing and flashing fire
When he opened his mouth you saw
Sharp teeth like swords
And after that he had a stretch and gave a big roar
On his back were pointy scales the colours
Were dark red and some are bendy
The sight of the dragon was a glamorous view.

William Endean (9)
Francis Baily Primary School

WINTER'S FALLING

It was a cold and crisp winter's night,
When the snowman gave me a fright.
He stood there tall and white,
Like a ghost in the night.
The wind grew strong with fright,
The snow fell silently on the freezing floor,
The moon shone gleaming in the night,
The hedgehogs ran to hibernate in their nests.
It's time for winter's near.

Rianna Marshall (8)
Francis Baily Primary School

FRIENDS

Friends are kind.
Friends are playful.
Friends are cheerful.
Friends are friendly.
Friends are forever.
Friends are good friends.
Friends are happy.
Friends are to play with forever and ever.
Friends are to talk to.
Friends are to sit next to.

Stewart Pearce (8)
Francis Baily Primary School

SEASONS

Summer is the warmest month of the year
It is hot and the sun is steaming.
Winter is the coldest month
It is freezing, it is frosty.
Spring in spring all the leaves fall to the ground.
Autumn is when all the leaves change colours.

Rhiannon Duckett (8)
Francis Baily Primary School

THE DRAGON

There's a dragon in my bed
A fire-breathing ugly monster.
There's a dragon in my bed
The dragon is coming after me
I saw it had a green tail and sparkly scales
It said I have a large splinter in my tail
I pulled it out
'Thank you' said the dragon.

Michael Panting (8)
Francis Baily Primary School

DRAGONS

Steaming dragon
Big teeth shine
Cave. Red-hot
Slimy monstrous Vory
Scales
Big dragon.

Victoria Kingston (9)
Francis Baily Primary School

SUMMER

It was very hot outside in summer
The leaves suddenly started to change like a rainbow on the trees
So the boy shouted 'Mummy can I go outside now with my friends?'
'Yes you can go out to play with your friends now.'
'Thanks Mum can I go on my bike?'
'Yes you can.'
'Thanks what time shall I be home?'
'Twelve o'clock.'
'Yes Mum.'
So the boy went out to play and the boy lived happy ever after.

James Ruczynski (8)
Francis Baily Primary School

THE VOYAGE

The voyage started long away
It didn't take us very long
To travel far away.
We packed the case and said goodbye
To all who loved us both.
We spent the night under the stars
Then carried on our way
To hill tops and valleys
Then we went on search of
Fun and when we had enough
Of it we'd sit still in the sun
And then one day we
Had to say our voyage had
Been done. We travelled home
We'd had our fun until another day.

Christopher Thomas (11)
Kintbury St Mary's School

I'M GOING ON A VOYAGE

I'm going on a voyage
But I don't know where
Maybe to sail the seven seas
Or even to Spain.

I'm going on a voyage
But I don't know where
I might sail round the Thames
Or even to the North Pole.

I'm going on a voyage
But I don't know where
I think I'll just stick
To the bath tub and
Pretend to sail!

Alex Dixon (11)
Kintbury St Mary's School

THE TORNADO

Hot and cold air join together,
This is the beginning of bad weather,
The tornado has formed
This is the beginning of a storm,
Wandering, whistling and winding,
Smashing, crashing and destroying
The path behind is decimated
In front is fear and panic,
Slowly the storm decreases
Everything is left in pieces.

Jake Noden (11)
Kintbury St Mary's School

SPACE JOURNEY

We were strapped to our seats
And the countdown began
10, 9, 8, 7, 6, 5, 4, 3, 2, 1
Blast-off!
We shot into the sky
And flew past the birds
Into space.

The stars dazzled and gleamed
And the Earth looked enormous
The ship flew over the moon
Then my partner and I zoomed down
And landed on the moon.

I stepped out
And looked around
I took hold of the flag
And planted it into the moon.

Jack Bellmont (11)
Kintbury St Mary's School

CHRISTOPHER COLUMBUS

When Christopher Columbus
Sailed the sea
He and his men found
That the world was round
People laughed at him,
Saying don't be daft,
So he told people to sail,
Round the world and he was proved right.

Zara Smith (10)
Kintbury St Mary's School

NORTH POLE

'Hurry up Spike we're going to be late'
All our luggage is waiting at the front gate
We're going on a journey on a side car and bike,
Just me, my luggage and my dog Spike.

We're going to the North Pole it's going to be cold,
There's going to be polar bears there well that's what I've been told.

I'm here at the North Pole and everything's quiet and still
We haven't seen a polar bear yet but I'm sure we will.

We better go home soon we're running low on food
I even had a nibble on a bone Spike had chewed
On the way back I saw a polar bear
I wish I had a warm coat like that to wear.

I hope Spike will like his new found mate
But it was rather tricky getting him through the front gate.

I'll remember this voyage it was the best I've ever had
To have brought back a polar bear I must have been mad.

Lucy Anstie (9)
Kintbury St Mary's School

MARCO POLO - 'THE MAN'

Marco Polo set sail to China, he invited Magellan and Reilley
They made their way around the world, this interested people highly.

Polo was a Venetian traveller, together with his uncle and father
They served the Mongolian Emperor and were workers in his parlour.

There was conflict between Chinese and Japanese troops on the
border of a state in Japan,
It lasted until the Japanese surrendered and Polo was named 'The Man'.

William Hutchins (11)
Kintbury St Mary's School

THE JOURNEY TO SCHOOL

Our school journey is long,
While we're in the car the radio is usually belting out a song
My sister is usually reading a book,
And I keep taking a look
At the clock to see what time it is
As we arrive at my sister's school
I watch a boy kicking his football
My sister gets out,
And has to shout,
Her goodbyes through the sound of cars
As we drive on,
My mum's fingers go pom, pom as she waits for the traffic to move
I think of the things I'm hoping to do that day,
I know that in the car with my mum is where I want to stay,
As we get into Kintbury,
We see all the children from my school,
As I get out of the car I start to run,
Because I know school has just begun.

Ellen Ireland (9)
Kintbury St Mary's School

INSIDE THE VOYAGE OF WAR

Inside the voyage, lays the coldness of war
Inside the coldness of war, lays the braveness of the voyage
Inside the braveness of the voyage, lays the death and hunger of war.
Inside the death and hunger of war, lays loving hearts in the voyage.
Inside the loving hearts of the voyage, lays the sadness of war.
Inside the sadness of war, lays the voyage,
Inside the voyage, lays the . . .

So let there be peace.

Stephanie Newland (11)
Kintbury St Mary's School

A Trip On A Ship

We all went sailing on the sea
My mum, my dad, my brother and me,
We sailed all the way across to Spain
But the sun didn't shine
It started to rain.

To stop getting wet we stayed on our ship
But some other passengers went on a trip,
We played some games and swam in the pool
Then we went on the deck for a game of boule.

It then stopped raining and we went outside
So we all went off to paraglide.

It was then getting late so we thought we would go home
I was so hungry I nibbled my dog's bone.

I enjoyed my voyage it was really great
I only wish I had brought my mate.

Victoria Hemphill (10)
Kintbury St Mary's School

The Voyage Of Night

Away, away over the hills and dales,
I sail on and on.
Through the night we swim
Travelling to the forsaken day.

The lands of the dreams are far from forbidden,
They entice to all to come in,
And further on you go and still the dream is far from finished
And then all is awash and . . .
Gone.

Helen Rivett (10)
Kintbury St Mary's School

A JOURNEY INTO HISTORY

The silence of the engines,
Until zero when the roar sounds like a wild animal,
Looking back you see an orb, which is Earth,
Soon you are there and your patience leaves you like a child waiting
                                        for Christmas,
Once you get out thoughts abandon you in disbelief,
Even though you don't know it the entire world is watching you,
Your words captured for all eternity,
'One small step for man, one giant leap for mankind'.

Jack Thorp (11)
Kintbury St Mary's School

SUPER SPACE

I am in a powerful rocket
Travelling into space
I sit and shut my eyes
We are going at an incredible pace
I am heading for another planet
High up in the sky
Looking out of the window
Watching the world go by
At the end of my journey
What will I find?
Maybe a lasting image
That I can keep in the back of my mind.

Vicky Crook (9)
Kintbury St Mary's School

?

Why is Mars called Mars?
So we can eat it.
   What is the moon?
   A piece of cheese.
Why does a rainbow form?
To show us to the gold.
   Why do we have electricity?
   So the world goes round.
What are eyes for?
To make us pretty.
   What is the flower made of?
   Multicoloured fluff.
What is the Earth?
A giant marble.
   Where do we come from?
   A tiny alien.
What is water pressure?
The thing that keeps me down.
   What is rain?
   God's cry.
Why is the world round?
For bouncing on the ground.

Zoë Hammond (10)
Sandy Lane Junior School

RIDDLE

I'm reflected white,
Hard and bumpy,
I'm seen all over the world
I'm not alone at night.

Jaun Burden
Sandy Lane Junior School

WHAT ... HOW ... WHY ...?

Why do we eat?
Because we're hungry.
What is wind?
When a butterfly flaps its colourful wings.
Why is time so short?
Because Father Time is short.
Why does it rain?
To wash away the germs that play.
How do you cut the air?
With the giant pincers of a scorpion's claw.
How does a rainbow form?
With the multicoloured pots of paint.
What is a dream?
A fluffy white cloud full of thoughts.

Sam Sweetzer (10)
Sandy Lane Junior School

POEMS

I would like to sleep on the clouds.
I would like to ride on a dragon's roar.
I would like to taste electricity.
I would like to taste the ghost of power.
I would like to paint the song of an octopus.
I would like to taste the gods.
I would like to draw the sound of an aeroplane.
I would like to taste the storm.
I would like to eat the bike's handle bars.
I would like to draw the sound of the howling wind.

Jamie Osborn (10)
Sandy Lane Junior School

DAMAGE

Spray, spray, spray!
Who is there?
Graffiti on your garage,
It's not fair!

Knock, knock, knock!
Who can it be?
'Someone's broke your car Miss,
And stolen your bronze key!'

Click, click, click!
What is that?
Scratching can be heard,
By a noisy, fluffy cat!

Bang, bang, bang,
Who, where, what?
Some things are so unfair,
And cause loads of damage.

Michelle Riordan (11)
Sandy Lane Junior School

ORANG-UTAN

Your fur is like orange autumn leaves,
You swing from branch to branch.
You eat tropical bananas,
You live high in the trees,
You groom your friends.
Just like an orang-utan
Oh you are one!

Martin Dixon (10)
Sandy Lane Junior School

I Remember . . .

I remember looking at my fat guinea pig,
He is big.
I remember looking at my easy homework,
I did it quickly.
I remember looking at my teacher,
She is very nice.
I remember looking at my best friends,
We have fun together.
I remember looking at a very sharp paper cutter,
Thinking I must not touch.

Matthew Bean (8)
Sandy Lane Junior School

What . . . Why . . . ?

What is the sun?
A glowing football.

What is a tree?
A wrinkly old man.

What is a piece of paper?
A pancake with honey.

Why are glasses clear?
They are made by Jack Frost.

Why are roses red?
People prick themselves on them.

Joe Scantlebury (11)
Sandy Lane Junior School

QUESTIONS?

What is your stomach?
Disgusting!
    Why does the wind blow?
    It's his job.
Why do animals shed their skin?
It was uncomfortable.
    When does it rain?
    When it wants to.
How do you use objects?
With your fingers.
    How do you return from the dead?
    You can't.
How long is a piece of string?
However long you want it to be.
    How dangerous is nature?
    However dangerous it gets.
Why is the sun bright?
It's not dull.
    Why are we alive?
    Thank the apes.
Why do we have names?
God forgot us.
    Why do I have to end this poem?
    My teacher wouldn't let me carry on.

Christopher Merton (10)
Sandy Lane Junior School

GORILLA

The gorilla is a funny thing,
In the trees it likes to swing.

The mountain gorilla the biggest of all,
They are humungus definitely not small.

In the trees all the time,
Eating fruit that tastes so fine.

Now it's coming to the end,
What you know about gorillas will depend.

Ethan Fuller (10)
Sandy Lane Junior School

COLOURS

Purple penguins pick pink poppies,
Orange octopus out of the ocean,
Blue blobs bring biscuits,
Green grumpy goats gobble gorgeous green grass,
Pink pelicans play pickey pipe,
Brown badgers bike on beaches,
Red robber Roger rakes rusty roads,
Yellow yo-yos yakked yesterday,
White wildman walked westwards wildly with wisdom,
Black bats bring bloodberries,
Gold gates grab grapes,
Silver sausages, sizzle sadly,
Peach people pick purple pips,
Ruby rings run rapidly,
Violet vases vote,
Lemon leeks look left lazily,
Chocolate cats can't catch Coke cans calmly,
Grey ghosts gamble,
Mauve mums measure metres madly,
Fawn father fix foxes frightfully in February.

Kelly Faulkner (10)
Sandy Lane Junior School

I WOULD LIKE TO . . .

I would like to . . .
    Eat the smell of mint,
    Smell the colour green,
    Touch the strength of a tiger,
    Hear the god and goddess speak.

I would like to . . .
    Paint the sky glittery silver
    Watch a pencil run an egg and spoon race
    Draw a picture of air
    Smell the taste of soup.

I would like to . . .
    Take home a jar of lightning
    Make a sculpture of air
    Touch a cup that isn't there
    See the Mr Nobody.

I would like to . . .
    I would just like to . . .

Jessica Johnson (11)
Sandy Lane Junior School

A SNOWY DAY

When the snow is on the ground
And swirling round and round and round
I love to see the swirl of the flakes
They have wonderful patterns, colours and shapes
When they melt the patterns dissolve
A snowman needs to be made in a hurry
While the snow is still in a flurry.

Rebecca Clayton (7)
Sandy Lane Junior School

THE A - Z OF ME

Autumn A is for Autumn yellow leaves falling, the season I like best,
Breakfast B is for breakfast, Mum makes pancakes with honey.
Carrots C is for carrots, a vegetable I hate.
Dad D is for Dad, he works in Hong Kong.
Everyday E is for everyday I miss him.
Football F is for football I like to play.
Good G is for Good, I try to be.
Hong Kong H is for Hong Kong my country.
I is for me, my name is Jason.
Jackdaw J is for Jackdaw, a book I like.
Kalvin K is for Kalvin, he is my older brother.
Ling L is for Ling, she is my cousin
Mum M is for Mum I love very much.
Naughty N is for naughty, of course I never am.
October O is for October for my birthday month.
Pancakes P is for pancakes, my favourite food.
Quiet Q is for quiet, which I am.
Red R is for red, is my favourite colour.
Sunday S is for Sunday, my favourite day.
Tea T is for tea, I like to drink.
Umbrella U is for umbrella, which I take when it rains.
Very V is for very, I am very good at art.
Watermelon W is for water melon, is my favourite food.
Excellent X is for excellent, Mrs Joyner says I am.
Yellow Y is for yellow, the colours of the sun
Zebra Z is for zebra, my favourite animal.

Jason Chung (8)
Sandy Lane Junior School

I Would Like To . . .

I would like to . . .
    Taste the sound of a fluffy white cloud
    Feel the fox's worried cry.
    Touch the warmth of the sun as it sets
    Paint the sadness of divorce
    Collect samples of the clear blue sky.

I would like to . . .
    Draw the wailing of a poor man's plead
    Make a robe of love
    Smell a hedgehog's cheeky laugh
    Hear a witch's magic powers
    Feel the happiness of a rich person's glee.

I would like to . . .
    Taste the sound of the rustling trees
    Paint all the love in the world
    Colour the beauty of a star
    See the cry of a dying mammal
    Create a potion of evil.

Emily Hawkes (10)
Sandy Lane Junior School

Warm Days

On warm days I go out to play
I can jump around all day
I can lie on the beach and play in the sand
With ice creams, lollies and long cold drinks
Lunch is salad and more ice cream
Round and round, my day is a dream.

Martin Carpenter (7)
Sandy Lane Junior School

I REMEMBER . . .

I remember . . .
    Looking at cars driving slowly along our narrow road
    Looking at my cat running up a tree, trying to catch a bird
    Looking at my big electric train sitting in my playroom,
    Looking at the clear blue sky on hot summer's day.

I remember . . .
    Tasting a scrunchy, red apple
    Tasting a sharp lemon down in Year 1,
    Tasting a lovely orange carrot,
    Tasting a hot dog with delicious onions.

I remember . . .
    Smelling new paint in my bedroom
    Smelling McDonald's when I am hungry
    Smelling newly cut grass in our field
    Smelling chicken pizza, ready for me to eat.

I remember . . .

Brendon Moss (8)
Sandy Lane Junior School

A HOT DAY

I love a hot day
You can play on the beach with all your friends
Swimming in the sea for hours on end
Going to the fairground on all of the rides
Being with special friends all of the time
No jobs or homework to do
Just spend the whole day with you - my friends.

Hannah Boon (7)
Sandy Lane Junior School

MY HAMSTER

I have a hamster
Who comes out at night.
Sometimes he appears
And gives me a fright.
He has a small nose
To sniff his toes,
He has big black eyes
Like cherry pies,
He likes to play
In his spinning ball,
He knocks the kitchen door
And the wall.
He rolls around
All over the place
As if he was
In a race.

Sadie Griffiths (10)
Sandy Lane Junior School

A COLD DAY

It means scarves, gloves and hats
White snow falling down
Slipping, sliding, falling over
Throwing snowballs at each other
Building snowmen with coal for eyes
Eating nice hot pies and drinking hot chocolate
I love a cold day!

Zachary Benham (8)
Sandy Lane Junior School

CHRISTMAS

I woke up one morning and looked outside
It was snowing
I opened my calendar and it was on the 24th
I got dressed and played in the snow
I saw a robin and a fox, they were lonely
My mum said, 'Do you want to go to the woods?'
'Yes,' I said, so we went.
I saw wonderful things
I went home and had a mince pie
And went to bed
The next morning it was . . .
Christmas!

Rhiannon Comerford (9)
Sandy Lane Junior School

A SNOWY DAY

Waking up early one dark morning
Fog on the ground, snow flying around
Cold, windy and snowing - we could hear bells
Dressed up warm and cosy we rushed to build Sid the Snowman
The bells grew louder and louder and then!
We saw a red hat, red coat and black boots
Guess who?
All on a snowy day!

Tamsin Horne (8)
Sandy Lane Junior School

WEATHER

Winter
Winter can be cold and wet
Winter can be snowy and have sparkling ice
Winter is frosty, windy damp and foggy,
Sometimes it rains hailstones and soon it starts to snow and snowflakes
Come drifting down
Sometimes there is thunder and lightning.
It can be muddy, there can be gales.
That's why no one knows what's going to happen next.

Summer
Summer is sunny, summer is bright
Summer is hot and breezy,
Summer has a bright sky
Sometimes there is a rainbow,
People pack bags to go on holiday
I wonder what is going to happen next.

Cally Trotman (9)
Sandy Lane Junior School

THE STORM

Bucketing with rain,
Rain tapping on the ground.
People wet,
Everybody wet.
People complaining everywhere,
The storm was frightening.

Simone Platt (7)
Sandy Lane Junior School

THE STORM

The storm arrived late in the night
With hammering rain that felt like nails
The wind blew hard and very loud
With whooshing and whistling all around
The thunder was scary and the lightning was too
I couldn't sleep in case it got me too, I thought it was a nightmare
But here I am safe and sound,
It is very wet outside but it's very warm inside.
Safe with my family.

Robert Myers (8)
Sandy Lane Junior School

SHARKS

Swimming predators
Swimming through the sea,
Big or small,
Sneaking behind prey,
Surfacing for a breath,
Rolling its eyes back,
Opening his eyes back to the normal way
Jaws snapping, catching fish,
Suddenly attacks
A loud scream
Blood covers a patch of the sea.

Kirk Nevard (10)
Sandy Lane Junior School

THE WATERFALL

Trickling waterfall
Splashing everywhere
Looks like green glass
Everyone stops and stares
From the top to the bottom
It falls to the ground
The glistening water
Splashes down
To form a great foam
Of a kind
Then slowly calms down to carry on down the river.

Stephanie Reynolds (10)
Sandy Lane Junior School

MY RABBIT

I have a rabbit
Snuffles is his name
We bring him in each evening
And he has a little game.
Snuffles is sometimes naughty
And chews my mum's mat
She comes into the kitchen door
And screams, 'That's enough of that!'
But he is very cuddly
And I still love him!

Emily Murphy (7)
Sandy Lane Junior School

WHAT IF . . . ?

What if my pants fall down in DT?
What if I walk into a lamppost in the middle of the path?
What if I go swimming and a shark bites me?
What if a bomb blows up France?
What if aliens take over the world?
What if people turn into monsters and monsters eat people?
What if the school falls down and teachers die?
What if the 3M collapses and destroys England?
What if Big Ben never stops ticking?
What if the Statue of Liberty came to life?
What if the president died in an aeroplane crash?
What if I saw somebody fly into air?
What if somebody kills me?
What if I disappear in bed?
What if my head gets stuck in the toilet?
What if my head gets blown off?

Samuel Hughes (9)
Sandy Lane Junior School

SNOWY DAY IN FINLAND

Finland in December is a wonderful place
Skiing each day at a slow pace
The snow is fresh, soft and powdery
The weather is cold, frosty and clear
Writing messages in snow with icicles
The patterns in snowflakes I could watch for hours
Jumping in snow hills with my brand new wellies
Snow is white and creamy and I love it!

Chiara Milford (8)
Sandy Lane Junior School

THE CHINESE ZODIAC

First came rat,
The smallest of them all,
He was cute, furry and had a very long tail.
Next came water buffalo,
Big and grand,
Then came tiger the loudest in the land.
Hare came after tiger,
Bouncing all around,
Dragon came next,
Flying up and down with a bound.
After dragon came snake,
Slithering in the grass,
After snake came horse,
Galloping very fast,
After horse came sheep,
She's coming through beep, beep!
Monkey was swinging from tree to tree,
Dog came running after monkey.
Rooster came next, cock-a-doodle-do!
And last but not least, pig came through.

Rosalyn Land (8)
Sandy Lane Junior School

I REMEMBER ...

I remember tasting mint sauce and it was disgusting.
I remember tasting brussel sprouts, they were horrible.
I remember tasting curry, it was lovely.
I remember tasting sweets, they were delicious.
I remember a hot day in the summer, it was boiling.
I remember going to the park, it was great fun.

Hayley MacKay (7)
Sandy Lane Junior School

WHAT IF . . . ?

What if a monster puts a bomb in my sandwich?
What if I fall off a cliff?
What if the playground turns into a mud pond?
What if the world blows up?
What if pencil cases turn into giant ants?
What if my pen eats me?
What if giant scorpions take over the world?
What if I fall down my toilet?
What if there's a volcano and it blows the school up?
What if my shoes eat my legs and my fingers eat my arms?

What if the school is made out of bubbles?
What if the chairs melt and the stars eat the moon?
What if there's a trap in my dictionary and one of the words eat my
                                                              bed?
What if birds could not fly and the sky turned yellow?
What if giant frogs rob a bank?
What if elephants turn into baby ducks?
What if my poster of a wrestler pops out and takes over the world?
What if my mum's freezer comes alive and eats our house?
What if a hippo eats every person on Earth?
What if I get my ear pierced and my ear blows up?

Scott Whiting (9)
Sandy Lane Junior School

SHARK

Swimming slowly through the sea,
Ready to look for tea,
Swimming slowly ready to kill,
Open jaw ready to eat
Shut jaw eating the feast.

Oliver Tomlinson (10)
Sandy Lane Junior School

WHAT IF . . . ?

What if a snake eats my lunch?
What if my teddy turns into an alien?
What if my mum turns into a baby?
What if my teacher has too much to drink?
What if the classroom turns into a castle?
What if a boy turns into a king?
What if a pig is a bird?
What if the moon turns into the planet Mars?
What if I died, oh no?
What if my house blew up when we were asleep?
What if the windows were made out of bricks?
What if the toilets were blocked?
What if my pants fall down in PE?
What if the teacher had magic powers?
What if the sky was red and turned into cheese?
What if Big Ben came back to life?
What if things appeared on the board?
What if a boat could talk?
What if a teacher got arrested?
What if a book did my work for me?

Nicola Osborn (9)
Sandy Lane Junior School

HEAVEN

H   oly people sing and dance,
E   verybody being helpful
A   ngels burst out with peace
V   iolets grow with a sweet scent,
E   ven God lives up there,
N   asty people don't go there.

Aaron Booton (10)
Sandy Lane Junior School

THE JEDI

Once I was a Jedi
Travelling in my spaceship
When I came upon the enemy
We had a long battle,
Lasers shooting all ways,
Then I remember my light sabre
Which meant I could win
One strike with my weapon
Made me victorious
And once more I could
Continue on my travels.

Daniel Cartledge (11)
Sandy Lane Junior School

I CAN...

I can play football.
I can make games up.
I can ride a bike.
I can run fast.
I can write.
I can tell the time.
I can swim around coral reefs.
I can eat a large portion of chips.
I can sleep for a long time.
I can play games.
I can ...

Perry Hann (9)
Sandy Lane Junior School

THE SAFARI

The safari is all very quiet,
Quiet as can be,
The hippo, the rhino and the elephant
Are all in the shade of a tree.
The lion is rolling around,
Making not a sound
The elephant is drinking water
His trunk looks like it's getting shorter
As it sinks into the water.
All of a sudden, there is a mighty *bang!*
And all of the animals suddenly ran.
Up through the bushes, the hunters appeared.
One of them had a big, brown beard!
From behind a tree, the cheetah crept,
Taking every careful step.
Looking around to see who's there
Taking a swipe,
But nothing is there.
There comes a shout, and a scream of help,
From one of the hunters,
There comes a yelp . . .
He's dead!

Caroline Land (10)
Sandy Lane Junior School

BEING GOOD

Today I am funny,
Today it's oh so good,
Today is very, very sunny,
Today I am going to be good.

Today I am sleepy,
Today is not so great,
Today I think it's raining
But I'm still going to be good.

Amy Harding (8)
Sandy Lane Junior School

THE CHINESE ZODIAC

Once there was a rat,
Who was naughty and black,
And he was going to Buddha's home,
On water buffalo's back,
He scampered off,
And then to Buddha
He said 'You're the first year,'
Rat was pleased,
Big buffalo was second,
He was pleased,
Tiger was next,
He growled but he was pleased,
Next was hare,
The dragon big and red,
The snake green and slimy,
Then was horse big and brown,
Then was sheep fluffy and white,
Then came monkey cheeky and fluffy,
Then was dog barking mad,
Then was rooster cock-a-doodle-do
Finally was pig very, very fat.

Oliver Rhodes (8)
Sandy Lane Junior School

FOOTBALL POEM

When I play football I have no doubt at all.

To the goal from my foot will be the ball.

The goalkeeper is jumping for the ball.

From the free kick which deflected off the wall.

When I shot, it went in the bottom corner hole.

From my foot the ball went in the goal.

Sam Whiting (11)
Sandy Lane Junior School

FIRSTS

First tooth,
First ball,
First rule.

First snow,
First goal,
First shoe.

First toy,
First speech,
First school.
First dress.

First day at the Juniors!

Helen Tallents (7)
Sandy Lane Junior School

COLD AND FROSTY

Snowman is very cold and frosty
With a carrot for his nose
And buttons for his mouth and big fat belly
A black hat for his big head
And Santa comes with all his presents for all
The children when they're fast asleep
He goes through the chimney and gets stuck
All the children heard and came
And pulled him out
He gives them presents and says
Good bye.

Daryl Molyneux (9)
Sandy Lane Junior School

GRAN'S PETS

In Gran's room she had . . .
Ten roosting chickens roosting on the bed,
Nine slimy snails making trails,
Eight spiders hanging on the bulb,
Seven smelly cats purring to pieces,
Six anacondas squishing the room,
Five deadly dogs, making an awful boom!
Four fat pigs being snorty,
Three rabbits hopping gracefully,
Two chirpy chicks
And one of *me*!

Robert Wellington (9)
Sandy Lane Junior School

What . . . Why . . . How . . . Where . . . ?

What are clouds?
Flying sheep.
    What is the sun?
    An orange.
What are your bones?
A pile of hot dogs.
    Why is wood hard?
    It doesn't want to snap.
Why does the moon change shape?
The mouse ate it
    Why do we have electricity?
    To make the world go round
Who do you cut the air?
With the wind.
    Where do rivers begin?
    From my tap.
What makes rain?
God's shower.
    What is gravity?
    Loads of glue.
Why do leaves fall off trees?
They want to feel the ground.

Callam Harding (10)
Sandy Lane Junior School

CHRISTMAS

Christmas decorations are shiny and smart,
Christmas trees are spiky and like a dart
Everything is beautiful, lovely and clean
Everything is like a very nice dream.

Christmas has started,
Presents and parties
Music and dancing into the night,
Singing and laughter
Raising the rafter
Have yourself a very nice time.

Corinne Farmbrough (8)
Sandy Lane Junior School

MY WHAT IF POEM

What if I get square eyes and everything is square?
What if I eat a bomb and I blow up?
What if I fall off a cliff and die?
What if Tony Blair dies?
What if I fall over and break my leg?
What if my house blows up and I am homeless?
What if a leaf falls on my head?
What if I go to swim in the sea and a shark bites me?
What if I walk into a lamppost?
What if my swimming shorts slip off when I am swimming?
What if a dragon eats me?
What if I fall down the toilet head first?
What if I get stung by a scorpion?
What if giant ants take over the world?
What if somebody bombs me in a Spitfire?
What if I get attacked by a homing missile?
What if somebody beats me up?
What if somebody shoots me with a sniper rifle?
What if I turned into a zombie?
What if my heart keeps on beating really hard and blows out
                                    of my chest?

Declan Cronin (9)
Sandy Lane Junior School

I Wish . . .

I wish that it was always hot and sunny and it never rained.
I wish that we were all millionaires.
I wish I could have an Andrex puppy.
I wish I could have anything I wanted.
I wish we could go to space and have an adventure.
I wish I could fly high above the clouds.
I wish I could go on a TV programme.
I wish I could run at ninety miles per hour.
I wish I was a queen and I had slaves.
I wish I had the biggest house in the world.
I wish I had a limousine.
I wish that I could go to bed at whatever time I wanted.

Sophie Hamlin (9)
Sandy Lane Junior School

Space Poem

Ten, about to take off,
Nine, checking oil,
Eight, walking up the stairs,
Seven, oops! Forgot the keys!
Six, ah found them,
Five, running to the shuttle,
Four, going up the stairs,
Three, jump into the ship,
Two, do up my seat belt,
One, blast-off!
Zero, bye!

Sarah Moody (9)
Sandy Lane Junior School

WEATHER

Weather is hot and cold
Seasons are
Spring, summer, autumn, winter.

Spring is when all of the flowers pop out
And out come the squirrels out to play.

Summer is when it's hot and people play
And sit in the sun eating ice creams.

Autumn is when all of the brown crispy leaves
Fall off of the tree onto the frosty grass.

Winter is when it's cold and frosty and sometimes sparkling
Snow falls down.

Siân Offen (10)
Sandy Lane Junior School

SPACE POEM

S   atellites circling the moon
P   lanets orbiting the sun
A   strounauts sent up in rockets
C   osmic dust all around
E   arth, third from the sun.

S   pace probes out there,
P   atrolling the empty space
A   steroids zooming round
C   utting through nothing
E   arth close to Venus.

Jake Rhodes (10)
Sandy Lane Junior School

SPACE

Space, wonderful space,
Shooting stars, milky ways,
Still planets, roaring rockets,
Spinning spacecrafts,
Angry aliens try to kill me!
Have you been to space?
You should it's cool,
I went with school,
I went in my imagination.

Now you've been there tell me what you saw,
Suns, galaxies, moons,
Nine planets did you know Pluto is the smallest?
I saw another astronaut or was it an alien!
Who cares?
I walked on the moon with Neil Armstrong
And Buzz Lightyear!
The last name is not true.

Kelly Stockinger (9)
Sandy Lane Junior School

WEATHER

Monday - black clouds fill the air,
Tuesday - rain falls down,
Wednesday - thunder, lightning crashes down,
Thursday - snowflakes fall,
Friday - a thick blanket of snow covers the ground,
Saturday - blizzards whiz everywhere,
Sunday - sun shines brightly.

Megan Holgate (10)
Sandy Lane Junior School

WEATHER POEM

When the sun comes out it brightens the day
In all kinds of wonderful magical ways.
In the dark, black night the thunder appears
Banging its drum until it's light.
There's a blizzard, it's frightening the children away
The snow falling, onto the people down below
Touching the tip of their noses crouching low.

The icy air feels like one thousand knives
Stabbing you all over your body.
The sun comes out and fills the day with joy
As the nasty weather fades away
Sinking through the wet slimy mud
Through which all the kids would come.

Brittany Baverey (10)
Sandy Lane Junior School

WEATHER

W inter weather
I   ndoor season
N ever sunny weather
T   earing fences
E   ar splitting wind howls
R   eally horrid weather!

S   unny weather
P   retty buds
R   oses budding
I   n the spring
N   ot a chance of snow as
G   rowing plants start to spread.

Elliott Clark (9)
Sandy Lane Junior School

I WISH . . .

I wish that you were allowed to eat ice cream while doing your work
I wish that it is always sunny and only rains sometimes at night.
I wish for green grass everywhere with flowers growing.
I wish everyone went on Who Wants To Be A Millionaire? and
                                        everyone won one million.
I wish the world was made of Galaxy chocolate
I wish you only go to school when you feel like it.
I wish at school you never get homework but if you do you
                                        colour a picture.
I wish that if you want something you get it.
I wish every three weeks it snows but it is hot out.
I wish no one dies or gets hurt.
I wish you're allowed to bring pets to school.
I wish that I had a cinema in my house.
I wish everyone's car was a limousine.
I wish I had a bowling ally in my house.
I wish there was an ice rink in my house.
I wish you could go on holiday whenever you want without booking.
I wish that I lived near the seaside.
I wish that I could meet Leonardo Di Caprio.
I wish that we were allowed to live on any planet.
I wish you could eat anything and you don't have to go to
                                        Weight Watchers.
I wish there were no floods.
I wish pencils were made of lollipops.
I wish I could be on a TV program like Eastenders or Friends
I wish I was Britney Spears' sister.
I wish I was a pop star.
I wish I could meet Jack Ryder.
I wish I lived near Thorpe Park.

I wish I was Britney Spears.
I wish I could walk on the sky and clouds.
I wish no one gets hurt in a car crash.
I wish my dad lived with me.

Kali Green (9)
Sandy Lane Junior School

THE STORM

The storm began to flash and crash
It covered my window and rained all night.
It started to thunder and then flashed a light.
It blew over the bin, it blew the leaves off the trees
And the tree fell to the ground along with the leaves
The path was wet with water and mud drowning my beloved plants
The lightning hit the electric wire and darkness came crashing down
We hope the storm has gone!

Ieuan Tucker (8)
Sandy Lane Junior School

SNOWY WEATHER

I like snowy weather because I can go on my sled
Also because I can have a good sleep in my bed
I like to make a snowman with my friends
I like to make a slide that bends and bends
I like snow when it's crisp and white
And sometimes I get frostbite.
I like snow when it's deep and crunchy
I like being at home where it's warm and cosy.

Jordan Wallace (8)
Sandy Lane Junior School

WEATHER

W ind blowing trees down
E   lectric lightning
A boom of thunder
T ornado destroying everything in its path
H ailstones crash down
E   lectric cables crashing down
R aindrops drip down on people's heads.

W et puddles on the road
E   lectric lightning coming this way
A boom of thunder with the lightning
T ornado just gone by
H urricane in the Far East
E   nd of storm just be aware it could come back again
R ainbow outside.

Alexander Richards (10)
Sandy Lane Junior School

THE WEATHER SURPRISE

One dark morning when I woke up
Frost on the ground, snow flying around
It was foggy
I heard a noise like scraping metal
And tracked it to the scrap yard nearby
But it was just the workers working there
A big rainy drop fell on my head
So I went home and went back to bed.

Tom Smyth (7)
Sandy Lane Junior School

RAINDROPS

I'm stuck inside my house,
Because of the hailstones and rain,
It's not fair,
I want to be out there,
Running and having fun again!

    The rain's getting harder
    Like a dripping tap,
    I'm getting lonely and bored,
    So I sit upon Mum's lap!

Now the rain is crashing to the ground
Like bullets hitting a rock,
Oh I'm fed up of all this rain,
Stop! Stop! Stop!

    The clock is ticking, tick-tock, tick
    The hailstones are flicking, flick, flick, flick!

Gemma Millard (9)
Sandy Lane Junior School

RAIN

Smashing down,
Bouncing on the roof,
Floods all around,
Soaking wet.
Bouncing on the ground,
Splashing on our heads,
Banging on the windows,
Rain is tipping down.

Corran Wilson-Davies (8)
Sandy Lane Junior School

I WONDER . . .

I look up into the sky,
And wonder . . .
What if Jupiter was the great king,
Of the sky and Saturn was his bride,
Mercury, Earth and Mars would be princes
Pluto would be a princess.

I look up into the sky,
And wonder . . .
What if Uranus was a fearsome warrior
And Venus was a wonder woman,
Neptune would be wonder girl.

I look up into the sky,
And wonder . . .
What if the moon was lord of cold weather,
And the sun was the lordess of hot weather,
The stars were the lords and lordesses of the rainbow.

I look up into the sky,
And wonder . . .

Erin Tallents (9)
Sandy Lane Junior School

THE STORM

It was a storm
It poured and poured and poured
It was a night, on the road it was flooding
My sister cried and cried and cried.

It was a horrible storm
It poured and poured and poured
It was frightening
Outside there were dreadful floods.

Chelsey Day-Hutchins (7)
Sandy Lane Junior School

I REMEMBER

Looking at my cupboards door slowly creeping open,
Looking at the stars shining bright in the midnight sky,
Looking at the half moon slowly developing into full moon,
Looking at children playing happily in the school playground.

Tasting the lovely roast dinner on a Sunday afternoon
Tasting peanut butter sandwiches fresh in my lunchbox,
Tasting sour sweets which my grandpa gets from work,
Tasting the salty water in the big ocean.

Smelling the fresh air on the sandy beach,
Smelling the gassy petrol in the garage up the road,
Smelling the tulips growing in my back yard,
Smelling my clothes straight from the wash.

Touching the rough paws on my pet Kiara,
Touching the lumpy wall in front of my friends house,
Touching the soggy mud in the school playground,
Touching the curved handle of my cup.

Listening to Who Wants To Be A Millionaire? on the TV downstairs,
Listening to my mum and dad arguing when I'm in bed.

Lee Avis (8)
Sandy Lane Junior School

The Storm

The storm was hard and it was bucketing down
It got harder and harder and the wind came in and the window broke
The branches fell from the tree and the tree shook and shook
Until one branch fell down.

Julia McQuitty (7)
Sandy Lane Junior School

Rainbows

R   ain falls from the sky
A   utumn is nearby,
I   cy street beyond the trees,
N   ow the rain stops to dry,
B   eautiful colours fill the sky,
O   range, blue, green and red
W   ow look how the colours shine,
S   un has gone now and everything's dark.

This is the beauty of our seasons.

Grace Holt (9)
Sandy Lane Junior School

I Wonder What's Up There

Space is black as night who knows what's up there
Looking for a fright?
Maybe Martians from Mars that creep and weep
Pluto could have many mystical creatures
Aliens might be living on a silver moon
But really nobody knows!

Ben Stewart-Armstead (9)
Sandy Lane Junior School

I REMEMBER

Looking at wildlife crawling around,
Looking at the moon and sun sliding together,
Looking at the night lamp in my bedroom,
Looking at the chips burning.

Tasting the salt on the crispy bacon,
Tasting icing on a cake,
Tasting the coldness in the ice cream,
Tasting the vinegar on my chips.

Smelling the air of the great open sandy beach,
Smelling a peach lying on the cut grass,
Smelling the lovely air,
Smelling the sausages sizzling in the pan.

James Birchall (7)
Sandy Lane Junior School

STARS

Bright at night,
Such a wonderful sight,
In the pitch black sky,
Like lights they shine to light up the night.

Twinkling, sparkling
Beautifully made,
Like diamonds in an everlasting mine,
They are night-lights for owls
How lovely.

Kesi Johnson (8)
Sandy Lane Junior School

WINTER PLAYGROUND

I am trying to get the dead of winter off the trees
As the squirrel, all yellow and grey, leapt on the trees
The bean bags are in the toy shed and hoops as well
All the fir trees and their leaves
How they will stay all the time.

Yvette Harvey-Brown (7)
Sandy Lane Junior School

THE STORM

It was very frightening
I could not get to sleep
I tried to wake up my mum.
I couldn't get mum up
Because she fell into a deep sleep.

Andrew Quinn (7)
Sandy Lane Junior School

THE DRAGON

There's a dragon in our street,
He's as tall as the 3M building,
He's as fast as a racing car,
He's as slow as a worm,
He's as funny as a cat chasing a dog,
He's as hot as the sun,
He's as cold as the ice,
He's as small as a mouse.

James Singh (8)
Sandy Lane Junior School

I REMEMBER . . .

Looking out seeing my mum going out in her silver Lexus,
Looking out at the street lights flashing on and off
Looking at Hannah's yellow curtains while music is blasting out.

Tasting the boiling water in my red mug
Tasting the Wheetos that's making chocolate milk in my cereal
Tasting the ice cold ice cream on a summer's day
Tasting the Yorkshire puddings from the red-hot oven nice and crisp.

Smelling the nice summer morning dew
Smelling the nice cut grass in the summer from the lawnmower
Smelling the hot donuts straight from the grill.

Samantha Reid (7)
Sandy Lane Junior School

THE MONSTER UNDER MY BED

As smelly as a dustbin,
As spooky as Goosebumps,
As noisy as can be,
As tall as the sky,
As brown as chocolate,
As slimy as a slug,
As fast as a cheetah,
As fat as a classroom,
As hairy as an ape,
As spiky as a porcupine,
As brainless as a pig.

Thomas Ward (7)
Sandy Lane Junior School

I Remember . . .

Looking at a king with a crown on his head,
Looking at the football player with the ball,
Looking at the snow falling from the sky.

Tasting the pizza with things on it,
Tasting the bread with butter on it,
Tasting the chips with salt and vinegar.

Smelling the chocolate and cream,
Smelling the chips cooking in the oven,
Smelling the wet, green grass on the ground.

Touching the wet football in my hands,
Touching the tree far away in the mud,
Touching the window in the sun.

Listening to the owl in the night,
Listening to the bird singing alone.

Joshua Still (7)
Sandy Lane Junior School

What I Saw One Frosty Night

One frosty night, when the trees were swaying,
And the snow was gently falling on the ground
When the stars were up high in the sky
Mr Frost decided to come out
He frosted the cars,
He frosted the moonlit sky
He frosted the windows and trees,
He frosted the street until it twinkled like the stars,
And that's what I saw one frosty night.

Rochelle Medford (9)
Sandy Lane Junior School

MY WEATHER POEM

As I open my door,
I see a world of white and glitter
I almost want to go and explore,
But I know it is the same place as always
There are snowflakes falling gently to the ground,
There might just be a world inside each little one
As I step outside I get covered in white flakes of snow
As I sit there, I think there is a whole new world outside my door
But tomorrow I know this mystical place will be gone.

Grace Bryant (9)
Sandy Lane Junior School

WINTER PLAYGROUND

Cars, bars, leaves, trees and bin, bang like the wind,
Branches,
Then a car drives in,
Tarmac,
Keep the tarmac clean.

Joshua Gostage (7)
Sandy Lane Junior School

THE SNAKE

The long,
Shimmering,
Slithering,
Slimy snake
Moved to and fro
Across the grass.

Conor Lay (7)
Sandy Lane Junior School

I REMEMBER

Looking at the television lighting up the room,
Looking at the stars that shine overhead,
Looking at the soft sheet of clouds when on an aeroplane.

Tasting the soft toffee sinking into your jaws,
Tasting the greasy sausages frying in the oven,
Tasting the wobbly tangerine jelly bouncing smoothly.

Smelling the soothing scent of rubber,
Smelling the washing up liquid in the kitchen,
Smelling the delicious smell of birthday cake.

Joe Reardon-Morgan (8)
Sandy Lane Junior School

BRACKNELL

Bracknell is a very big place,
Swimming in the sports centre,
Bracknell is an old town and very busy.
Bracknell has many changes,
It is also modern.
Bracknell is noisy.

Kieran Raine (7)
Sandy Lane Junior School

SNOW

The snow is falling white and soft
Until it reaches the ground and settles
The snow is like a blanket of white,
Laying silently on the ground.

In the morning the ground is white
The children are playing with sledges,
And throwing snowballs around.
A snowman stands alone in a field of snow.

Elizabeth Allen (10)
Sandy Lane Junior School

THE MONSTER UNDER MY BED

There's a monster under my bed,
He's as smelly as a dustbin,
He's as fast as a speeding boat,
He's as hot as lava,
He's as cold as ice being thrown at you,
He's as tall as the Empire State Building,
He's as spiky as a needle,
He's as hairy as a baboon,
He's as loud as a million drums.

Sam Boultwood (7)
Sandy Lane Junior School

COMETS

C   omets are very cool
O   rbits around space
M   eteorites are like comets
E   normous comets
T   ravelling through space
S   craping the sky with its fishy tail.

George Totari (11)
Sandy Lane Junior School

WINTER PLAYGROUND

Birds are flying,
Crisp packets on the tarmac,
A squirrel is yellowy, medium grey,
Trees with no leaves,
A bin on the playground,
A tractor and car on the road,
The fence is wooden, mossy,
I saw logs,
And grass
I saw some girls and boys.

Christopher Asante (8)
Sandy Lane Junior School

SNAKES

Snakes slip and slide,
Their bodies go from side to side,
Tongues go in and out,
Skin of scales,
Skin so soft to touch.

Tom Offen (7)
Sandy Lane Junior School

THE MONSTER UNDER MY BED

There's a monster under my bed,
It's as tall as a tall building,
It's as spiky as a hedgehog,
As hot as fire,
As scary as a ghost,
And as dangerous as a dragon.

Georgina Mackin (8)
Sandy Lane Junior School

THE WILD WIND

I hate the wind that
Whistles.
The wild wind that's
Angry.
I hate the wind that's
Who I hate.
I hate the wind from
The North Pole.
I hate the wind that
Comes.
The wild wind that's
Who I hate.
I hate the wind that
Crushes.
I hate the wind that
Clatters.
The wild wind that's
Who I hate.
I hate the wind that
Falls.
I hate the wild wind, that's
Who I hate.
Do you hate the
Wild wind?

Claudia Beaney (8)
Sandy Lane Junior School

THE WIND

The wind whistles loudly
When I go to school I get cold
When it's Christmas, it is freezing
Our homes are frozen and cold
Ponds are icy
The frosty wind blows me about
And blows people about
I do not like it when it's loud
When it's freezing cold
It makes your ears cold
I do not like it,
It's too cold!
I hate the wind from the sky.
I just hate it.

Robert Johnson (8)
Sandy Lane Junior School

SNOW

The snow has started to fall
And the house is cold.
Everything is white
But me!
Is everyone cold?
Or is it only me?
However can this be?
I don't know but God does.
Now the snow has stopped falling
And all the enjoyment has gone for us!

Faraz Siddiqui (9)
Sandy Lane Junior School

THE WILD WIND

The powerful wind is crashing to the floor.
Like someone moaning on the shore
The strong,
Thunderous,
Boom!
The horrible gale coming near
We'd better hide before it's here
The flashing, noisy, weather thundering
Down, trying to get us.
Oh! Wind go away, please come
Back another day.

Lowri Roe (9)
Sandy Lane Junior School

WIND

Wind can ruin, wind can clash,
Now the wind will go and smash.
All the houses on the town,
Have their heads hanging down.
Wind is strong, wind is clear,
I wish I could kill it with a spear.
Wind can wreck and always blast,
Now the wind's running fast.
Wind can shatter, wind can roar,
I can't cut it with a saw!
Wind can bang and wind can boom,
Now the wind can run and zoom.

Jack Jefferies (8)
Sandy Lane Junior School

THE WIND

The wind is scary.
The wind is creepy.
The wind is weary.
The wind is freaky.

It sneaks around corners.
It glides through alleyways.
It blows out torches
And it flows around for days.

It can knock down buildings
It can start up tornadoes
But some are left standing
When you find a tornado.

But the summer breeze won't do anything bad
It's just like a nice cool drink
Or like your mum and dad
And it never ever thinks.

James Blyth (8)
Sandy Lane Junior School

WHEN THE WIND BLOWS

When the wind blows
It makes me shiver.
When it screams
It makes me quiver.
When I listen
It roars with laughter.
I know it must be here.

Katherine Clark (8)
Sandy Lane Junior School

NIGHT-TIME

I remember
Looking at the stars glowing in the sky,
Looking at the moon sparkling in the sky,
Looking at the dark planets in the night,
Looking at the car lights glowing on the road,
Looking at the glittering pond near the park,
Smelling the fresh air out of my window.

James Andrews (7)
Sandy Lane Junior School

MY FAVOURITE FOOD

That crinkly wrapper
That chocolatey smell
That big chunk of chocolate
Oh what a yummy thing
It's delicious, hard, sweet, tasty chocolate.

Sarah Lyndon (8)
Sandy Lane Junior School

THE GALE

The hail was like hard stone,
The thunder was like a black, dark blanket,
The hail was like the snow,
The rain was like spitting water,
The wind was like a hurricane.

Sarah Lobar (7)
Sandy Lane Junior School

The Monster Under My Bed

Help! There's a monster under my bed,
It's as fast as a leopard sprinting along the desert,
It's as hot as fire burning bright,
It's as loud as a lion roaring,
It's as smelly as a dustbin,
It's as tall as the BT Tower
It's as spiky as a hedgehog,
It's as fat as this school,
It's as hairy as a gorilla,
It's as crazy as a cat chasing a dog.

Katie Allen (8)
Sandy Lane Junior School

Winter Playground

The shed was full of games,
The birds were flying around the trees,
I saw a stone on the ground,
I saw an aeroplane flying,
I saw the fence,
I saw a big, long oak tree,
I saw a bench full of girls and boys,
I saw girls playing basketball.

Naomi Nyamaah (8)
Sandy Lane Junior School

I REMEMBER

Looking at the stars twinkling in the night sky,
Looking at the moonlit moon,
Tasting a fish, sweet and tasty,
Tasting bacon crunching in my mouth,
Tasting lemon tangy and sweet,
Smelling a flower sweet with nectar in the middle,
Smelling the oak tree old and wrinkly,
Smelling petrol from a motor car.

Adam McBride (7)
Sandy Lane Junior School

MIDWINTER POEM

The lifeless countryside, ice and frost
All the animals seem to be lost
The weather is sharp
Very cold and dark
The days are getting shorter
The nights getting long
All the little sparrows
Have long gone.
The ponds are sparkling
With all the ice
The animals are all hibernating
Including the little mice
Slippery surfaces, bleak winter days
Encrusted ice on cars, frozen shallow bays
Cold winter days into cold winter nights,
All the little animals tucked up nice and tight
Next comes the spring, sparrows all return
Animals out of hibernation
It's the summer's turn.

William Crane (10)
St George's School Windsor Castle

THE LUNAR ECLIPSE

The moon, a crystal orb,
Hanging in the starry sky,
Suspended amongst folds in the rich and spacious robes of night
Forever,
Doomed
To continue her celestial flight round the Earth,
Trailing him, bobbing in his wake,
Like a puppy, snapping at his heels,
But never drawing nearer no matter
How many steps she takes.

One evening in midwinter
Weary from her daily exertions
The moon rose full and cast a tired and bloodshot eye
Upon her slumbering quarry,
So blithe and breezy,
And blissfully unaware of her pursuit
And she gave a little sigh.

    I'm completely spent,
    I've had enough,
    Who'd mind or even notice,
    If I were to take a little break
    And catch maybe . . . forty winks?

And indeed she did, just closed her eye,
And darkness reigned over Earth and sky.

Stephen Purvis (11)
St George's School Windsor Castle

MIDWINTER POEM

Winter is a frosty night
As cold as it can be.
When it came down very hard
On that winter night
When it was the night-time
All the creatures hibernate
In the morn they're still asleep
And the windows are encrusted
And the presents were gone
The turkey was gone
And the pudding was gone
But one thing wasn't gone
Because it was New Year's Day!

Christian Jenkins (9)
St George's School Windsor Castle

ANT

Little ant on the floor
Going through an open door.
Where is it going? I don't know
Maybe it can see some snow.
The little ant lives underground
Never making any sound
It never ever goes to school
So it is quite a silly fool
Under tables, under chairs
Under children's teddy bears.
It could eat a big cream bun
The ant is the creature for everyone.

Edward Vaughan (10)
St George's School Windsor Castle

MIDWINTER POEM

In the bleak midwinter,
Slippery as ice,
Lifeless creatures run across,
The frosty ground today,
Sparkling ponds gleam through the land,
Every day and night.

Treacherous trees stand in their way,
As they walk through the cold winter's night
And it was like a cold creepy Christmas night.

And the iciness on the branches were encrusted,
There were children skating on the ice with sharp blades
Just sawing across the lovely frozen pond.

Razzak Mirjan (11)
St George's School Windsor Castle

MY TRAVELS

I have travelled near and far
I've seen many a thing
I've seen clouds like candy floss
And a land covered by sun.
I've seen trees that act like umbrellas
And a river rolling on high.
I've seen rocks tower like mountains
And moss cover a mile.
I've seen people with smiling faces
And men with sunken eyes.
I've travelled near and far
I've seen many a thing.

Sophie Everett (11)
St George's School Windsor Castle

MIDWINTER POEM

Midwinter is
Cold and foggy,
The sparkling grass
With frost lightly sprinkled.

The icicles are frozen stiff,
And the cars are
Encrusted with ice and frost
Waiting to be scrubbed off.

The wood looks lifeless,
All animals are asleep
Slippery paths and roads
To watch out for!

When you get inside
A freezing car
You turn into ice
And then get into a house quick!

The animals are lost
Wondering what to do
Because the food is
Gone or frozen.

Spring hurry up!

Henrietta Smethurst (9)
St George's School Windsor Castle

FROSTY DAY

If I woke up one frosty day
It would look so much like Christmas Day
If my car was covered with frost
To clean it would money cost
When I woke up I was so cold
And that's why
The sheets wouldn't fold
Because it is so cold
Today.

It is not always
Cold in winter
It can be very nice
But when I woke up
I was so cold
And that's why
The sheets
Wouldn't fold!

Liam Anderson (10)
St George's School Windsor Castle

MIDWINTER POEM

In the bleak midwinter long, long ago
In a little lifeless village
Frosty trees and a little lane
Once full with lovely little bunnies
And a little country gate with scruffy little robin
Sitting on the little gate whistling
A little tune like all robins do.

What shall the poor robins do
In the bleak midwinter long, long ago
In the lifeless village with
A scruffy little robin on a rooftop
Whistling a lovely tune.

Jessica Kelly (9)
St George's School Windsor Castle

GOBLIN

As the wind blows
In the dark night
The goblin strikes
As he claws his way
Through the rubbish bins
Around the dusty inn
He finds a tin of pineapple skin.

Through the rubbish bins he goes
Over the dusty road he goes
Over the curb into the inn
And there he finds a pin.

Back with the pin he goes
To his inn and finds a
Spider with some cider,
A goat with a croaky throat
And a goldfish with a float.
There he goes to bed
With a dizzy head.

Kyle Dunton (9)
St George's School Windsor Castle

MIDWINTER POEM

The bleak white snow
Covers the frozen ground
The trees are white, the roofs slippery
The sparkling frost are on the doorsteps
Frozen pond have sharp coverings
Children play with the frosty snow
The lifeless summer plants are
Dying away
The winter flowers
Are sprouting out.
Your solid hands are melting as you enter your house
Some animals are in a deep sleep
Squirrels are gathering their food
Snowball fights are being held
Lancashire stew is being brewed
In the heated kitchen.
In the morning the cars are like white dragons
With their eyelids closing and opening
The garages are protection for little carriages
Winter, oh winter is absolutely gone.

Kevin Cheng (10)
St George's School Windsor Castle

MIDWINTER

A queen looked out of her castle
Once on Christmas Day
When she saw a horse in a field
Eating his crunchy hay.

    A king looked out of his castle
    Once on Boxing Day
    To see a handful of children
    Out in a frosty field to play.

A child looked out of his window
Once on New Year's Day
To see a thick layer of snow
Out by Porlock Bay.

A cat went walking in a park
Going its own way
Going forward in time
To the end of May.

Sam Gough (11)
St George's School Windsor Castle

BOOKS

In the library
Or at home
About Santa or
The Millennium dome.
Words, pictures
Or maybe both
You must read them all
Please make an oath.
Big, small,
Never mind which
Look after them all
Don't keep them in a ditch
Don't bend them or throw them
Across the room
Or keep them in a cupboard,
With the broom
Keep them on a case,
And never fear,
If you need them,
They will always be near!

Madelene Fitzgerald (10)
St George's School Windsor Castle

A MIDWINTER VILLAGE

An icy road
Too slippery for cars to drive past
A frozen pond
Too lifeless for pond life
A snow-covered line
Too treacherous for trains
A bleak path
Too slushy for briny grit and salt
A roaring fire
Too warm for the snow to enter
A cold forest
Too freezing for an animal's resistance.

Edward Robinson (11)
St George's School Windsor Castle

BOARD GAMES

Board games to me are so much fun
Some are short, some run, run, run
There are many games such as Monopoly,
It is long but great for me
Scrabble is a game of words,
This game is not for nerds!
Another game is Pay-day
This game is so good that you can play it every day
If in a game you badly cheat
You deserve a very strong beat
If at game end, you have won,
Congratulations! Well done!
If you want fun go grab a game
Oh heavenly, heavenly board games!

Edward Frankl (9)
St George's School Windsor Castle

WINTER HORSES

As they gallop across the frosted fields
Curious eyes watch over them
Icicles dangle from frozen trees
As winter is drawing near.

Their eyes are full of fright and coldness
For snow is falling hard
But the stallion stands his ground
To protect his group of friends.

I wonder how they stand and stare
On the frosty frozen ground
Their feet are frozen up
For they are the winter horses.

Emily Gibbs
St George's School Windsor Castle

BUTTERFLY

A butterfly was flying through the air
And wow what colours he has
Watch there he goes flying through the air
Oh what a brilliant flyer
Oh I do wish I could fly like a butterfly
Oh and his wings look like flowers
Oh it looks like it just glides through the air
What a beautiful insect it is
But we've got to remember he is delicate
And so looks like a fairy
Or even the tooth fairy
Oh but I do wonder what does he eat
Does he eat air or what
Oh I do wonder.

Henry Crame
St George's School Windsor Castle

ANIMALS

There are lots of different animals in the world
There are fishes, mammals and lots of birds
Some eat meat, some eat grass
Some are slow, some are fast
Lots eat beetles and little bugs
Some live underground, some under rugs
Rabbits are my favourite along with guinea pigs
You can keep them as pets, but they don't like eating twigs
There are dogs, which I like too
They will play lots of games with you
Lions are hungry, they want to eat you,
Or little zebras are nice too
The males rest while females hunt
They only get up to eat the kill
And then go back to sleep when they have their fill,
I like pigs who eat a lot of swill!

William Crane (10)
St George's School Windsor Castle

THE SECRET LIFE OF A BUBBLE

The transparent film glistens like light,
It dithers here and there,
From left to right
The metallic colours shine inside,
The drop of water takes a ride.

The spherical globe shimmers in the sun,
It flounders and floats as though it's having fun
About to burst? About to pop?
Surface tension and stretchy skin on the top!

That tiny droplet expands with air,
Another bubble mingles to make a pair
The dancing duo descend at last,
As they emerge together
And disappear fast!

Alysia Lakhani (10)
St George's School Windsor Castle

THE ICE CAVERN

In the icy winter months
In the mountain's snow
An ice cavern a frozen beauty
Stays a cave of frost.

An ice glacier the cavern
Is with pools of frozen water
The icicles are like sharp spikes
Guarding the cave from intruders.

It never melts this ice wonder
Even in the summer
The light makes the ice
Look like crystals in the blazing sun.

In the winter a polar bear comes
He hibernates in here
And through the raging snowstorms
He snuggles up warm and cosy in there.

When winter ends he goes away
Another year has gone
And the patient ice cavern
Waits once more for the polar bear to return.

Nick Simmons (10)
St George's School Windsor Castle

A MIDWINTER POEM

As I walk upon this open grass
I see no green,
I see white
The white of . . . snow!

I stare at this amazing sight
Not realising what beauty I am in
I would like to stay, stand and stare
At this beauty that surrounds me.

People say we have no time to stand and stare,
But if we did we would glare,
At the squirrels, at the trees, at the sky.

Eventually we have to go back home
But every day that goes by,
I will think . . .
How
Rich
Am
I!

Sai Bachan (11)
St George's School Windsor Castle

THE RAINBOW

The rainbow shines high in the sky
With a pot of gold at each end
Its colours glow sending rays through the air.

The red is for roses easily picked out
The yellow is for sunflowers to grow tall and grand
The green is for jungle creepers hanging from branches old.

The blue is for oceans deep their waves rolling in ripples
The orange is for the sun providing powerful light
The indigo is for pansies never stopping as they grow.

The violet is for the shade of dark light in the night sky
The double rainbow is the one we all want to see
But it is the one that comes rarely.

George Christie (11)
St George's School Windsor Castle

CAT

Elegant ways of walking
Producing gorgeous strides
A king and queen it seems like
A duke or duchess inside.

Scratching, biting, clawing
A cat is all but that
Majestic ways of everything
Now that is a cat.

Elegant ways of walking
Producing gorgeous strides
A king or queen it seems like
A duke or duchess inside.

Playful as a kitten
Though keeping adult touch
Supreme ruler and commander
Well, maybe a bit too much.

Keara Cornell (9)
St George's School Windsor Castle

A TRIP TO ITALY

I really want to go to Italy,
I don't know where maybe to Sicily,
I said I'd like to go to Rome,
My sister wants to stay at home,
I'd like to go somewhere hot,
My mother said she'd rather not.

I've only been to one holiday,
I'd love to go even for a day,
My brother said he'd like to play,
My father said that he should stay,
To Italy I'm not to go,
Not without my parents say so.

I'd like to invite my find Lisa,
And we could visit the Tower of Pisa,
And I know she'd like to eat pasta,
And on the plane we'd go faster,
But when I asked if she'd go,
She turned around and just said no.

But now to Italy I can't go
Because everybody has said no,
But nobody has fulfilled my dream
I guess I'll sit and eat ice-cream
But now I'm upset
And I guess that's as far as I'll get!

Lilly Sayer (11)
St George's School Windsor Castle

Nufin' Like An English Breakfast

Oh an egg, an egg I spied
Of which I broke and then I fried
Of which the hen laid just for me
A delicious eggy odyssey.
Next the bacon now here's a treat
Do better by far than smelly feet.
Then I cook it on the grill
Oh how delicious, what a thrill!
To make it work just add toast
This will definitely make the most.
Take the bread very slowly
Make it sacred, make it holy.
At this point it seems that
You are in need of some baked beans.
Now to take it out the tin
Fill up the plate up to the brim.
Place it in the microwave
It's so good I've got a crave.
Now last but not least
To finish off this yummy feast,
A black pudding to add some flavour
This will work out in my favour.
Now at last it's on the plate
Oh how tantalising, oh how great!
Time to test it, here it comes!
Don't leave morsels, don't leave crumbs!
You want my opinion? Here are the odds
This English breakfast is the food of the gods!

Dominic Mellor (10)
St George's School Windsor Castle

DOWN AT THE SEASIDE

Down at the seaside the seagulls scream
Down near the seaside it's everyone's dream,
Down at the seaside the amusements are open
Down near the seaside the clocks shows ten.
Down at the seaside it is lunch,
Down near the seaside there is a lot to munch,
Down at the seaside there's people at the fair
Down near the seaside wind is blowing people's hair
Down at the seaside old ones are sleepy
Down near the seaside young ones at the fairground, creepy
Down at the seaside the moon is glowing
Down near the seaside the river's outward flowing.
Down at the seaside at night time people are snoring
Down near the seaside it's getting towards morning.
Down at the seaside I feel really cool
Down at the seaside I still go to school!

Edward Robbs (10)
Stockcross CE Primary School

FOOTBALL

My boring name is Graham Lee,
My dream's to play at Wembley,
I wish I were on a hat trick roll,
I wish I scored that golden goal.

Listening to the roaring crowd,
Makes me feel amazingly proud.
The football hero Graham Lee,
Has drifted into history.

Josh Beecroft (10)
Stockcross CE Primary School

WHY CAN'T SOME BIRDS FLY?

If penguins have wings
Why can't they sing?
If they can cry
Why can't they fly?

If ostriches have wings to fly
Why can't they learn to flutter up high?
And when some birds can't really run
The ostrich can and have so much fun.

So I really, really wonder why
Some birds just can't fly?

Antonia Beard (9)
Stockcross CE Primary School

RUGBY

The enemy hits me with a booming thud
I go flying into the sludgy mud,
A revenging punch hits him in the thigh.
The crowds are beginning to jump really high,
'Boo hiss!' the crowds jeer
'You two dismissed' shouted the ref without fear.
Me and him trudge off,
As I started to splutter and cough.
Oh boy you just wait
Next time buddy, it's *your* fate!

Nick Young (11)
Stockcross CE Primary School

A DAY AT SCHOOL

Bed.
Bed, breakfast.
Bed, breakfast, bus.
Bed, breakfast, bus, play.
Bed, breakfast, bus, play, lunch.
Bed, breakfast, bus, play, lunch, read.
Bed, breakfast, bus, play, lunch, read, club.
Bed, breakfast, bus, play, lunch, read, club, bed.

Matthew Rosell (10)
Stockcross CE Primary School

BUBBLES

I love bubbles in the bath
I love bubbles in the sink
But the bubbles I love best
Are the bubbles in my drink.

Rosa Macdonald (9)
Stockcross CE Primary School

TOFFEE

Sticky, squidgy, yummy toffee
You like to eat it with your coffee
Tasty, toothsome never ever gruesome
Sticky, squidgy, yummy, toffee.

Joanna Meads (9)
Stockcross CE Primary School

THE LONELY SCARECROW

Standing high on a hill
Stuffed with straw
Ragged shirt and torn gloves
Crinkled hat and boots
Mangled scarf and rusty pole
Swaying in the whining wind
Ripped trousers patches and all
Frayed coat and scruffy face
A dangling eye and cracked nose
Why do people really hate me?
Why do birds fly away?
But one creature likes me
And that's the hedgehog
Who lives under a pile of auburn leaves
Who has made his home all snug and
Warm.

Abigail Gostick (9)
Stockcross CE Primary School

SCHOOL DINNERS

Monday - what's to eat? Chicken's feet.
Tuesday - what's for dinner? Pig's liver.
Wednesday - what's the feast? The head of a beast.
Thursday - what's for lunch? Cow to munch.
Friday - what's the food? A frog being rude.
Saturday - yummy, at last - I've broken the fast!
Sunday - a meal to devour - the last hour before
We're back at school, shouting
We hate school dinners!

Tessa Chichester (11)
Stockcross CE Primary School

IT'S NOT FAIR

It's not fair that I have to go to bed
It's not fair that I always bang my head
It's not fair that I have to get up from my snugly, warm bed
It's not fair that I have to go to my dreary school with the dead
It's not fair that my mum took my bun
It's not fair that I can't have fun
It's not fair that I have to go home
It's not fair that I can't go to the dome
It's not fair that I have to go in the car
It's not fair that it's really, really far.
My boring life just isn't fair.

Victoria Brown (10)
Stockcross CE Primary School

THE VOYAGE

I travelled the sea,
I travelled the sky,
And what a trip oh my, my, my
As I travelled through the sky,
The stars would sparkle in my eye
The sea was rough, the sea was calm,
The fishes seemed to swim under my arm
The trip was good, the trip was fun,
Also there was lots of sun.

David-John Forword (10)
Stockcross CE Primary School

HAUNTED HOUSE

I went into the haunted house,
No one there, not a mouse,
Haunted stairway, haunted rooms,
Outside there are stony tombs.

Headless Nick on his horse,
Going round his haunted course,
Stinky smell everywhere,
Ghosts creep up and give me a scare.

Ghostly cows going moo,
Other ghosts shout
Boo!

Rosie Waterfield (10)
Stockcross CE Primary School

LIST OF FUN

Get out your rod,
Get out your reel,
Thread the line,
Attach the float,
Hook the worm,
Get out the keep net,
Get out the landing net,
Get out the bait,
Get out the weights,
Method
Have fun fishing!

Thomas Allen (11)
Stockcross CE Primary School

THE NIGHT SKY

The night sky is a jet-black, dark blanket
With little, twinkling silver specks.
The night sky is a black prowling cat
Sneaking up onto a little white bird.
The night sky has tiny gold fireflies
Dancing on a velvet blackened sheet.

The night sky as dark-grey clouds which dance,
Around on a small breeze that slowly moves.
The night sky has little white lights that twinkle all night long
The night sky says bye in the morning and
Hi in the evening,
I love the night sky
Good night from me.

Stephanie Townsend (11)
Stockcross CE Primary School

A TIGER

A tiger's eyes shine like diamonds
His teeth are made of flint,
His coat is made of silk,
His heart is courageous and bold.

His paws are made of iron,
His claws are made of steel,
His stomach must be very strong,
To digest that tasty meal!

Dora Eisele (10)
Stockcross CE Primary School

VALHALLA

'All aboard the ship
You're going on a treacherous trip
But you may take an unexpected dip in the attacking sea.'
Shouted Ziggi Viking to his men.

'Try not to roll or sway in case the ship you tip
At best you might bite your lip
For in the attacking sea you'll die, remember you can't fly!
On your menacing trip to Valhalla'.
Shouted Titus Viking to his gang.

Emily Reid (10)
Stockcross CE Primary School

MOTHER'S DAY

On Mother's Day I got up first,
Full of flowers I nearly burst.

Started breakfast right away,
For the surprise on Mother's Day.

Picked some flowers came right back,
To make the coffee rather black.

I like Mother's Day an awful lot,
Because I like my mum a *lot*!

Isabel Watterson (10)
Stockcross CE Primary School

I'M A CHIMNEY SWEEP

When I go to chimney sweep
My mother will always weep.
Why do you have to work like this?
Poverty and sickness,
Don't worry Mother, I'll make you money,
So you can buy us bread and honey.
What if you're crippled? What if you die?
Don't worry Mother do not cry.
Don't be sad
It's not that bad
This old Tim Ball,
Has no food, not at all
So go to bed,
And rest your head
I should be back with a wage
If I'm not dead.

Aimee Waters (11)
Whitelands Park School

AUTUMN

Autumn is a golden and dark brown,
It tastes like warm milk and buttered toast,
It sounds like leaves falling all day,
It looks like bare branches against yellow sun,
It smells like harvest, I'd say,
It makes me feel joyful and free.

Nicholas Buxey (7)
Whitelands Park School

THE VICTORIAN CHILD

V iolently they were hit with the whip
I nside the chimneys their clothes would rip
C arefully they would climb with a broom
T rying quickly to get down soon
O nly they have no mail
R obbing the money from the van by the rail
I nside they are very sad
A nd they're feeling very bad
N ow they have to steal their food.

C rying for money that is very rude
H orrible were their houses
I nside were woodlice
L ots of friends but not very nice
D o want food but can't pay the price.

Thomas Donnelly (10)
Whitelands Park School

SUMMER'S DAY

Summer is bright and yellow
Summer tastes like cold ice drinks
Summer sounds like lots of people chatting
Summer looks like a long row of yellow flowers
It smells like fresh green grass and fish swimming
In the open sea
It makes me feel happy.

Jessica Mcauley (7)
Whitelands Park School

VICTORIAN CHILDREN

There are children crying in the dark,
Al they could hear were the swings in the park
Sadness lies in the children's souls
They are playing on the rusty poles
Strict teachers, getting the canes,
Little children welling in pain
Daddies are slamming the doors
They want to work no more!
There was a boy who wasn't well
When he came in there was an awful smell!
A girl was sitting in a cold dark corner,
In the classroom there was a dirty border
The Victorian children starving to death,
The dirty pots was all that was left.

Frances Spreadbury (11)
Whitelands Park School

A VICTORIAN CHILD

It is cold and lonely
Dark and dismal
No food for long hours
Pollution leaves little air
Poor conditions
No money
Cut feet
Envy, upset, sad, ripped clothes
Cruelty, sorrow, illness
Why do we act as adults when it can lead to our death?

Aaron Webber (11)
Whitelands Park School

SCHOOLDAYS

Before school
Mum, Jessica is ill
Mum, I need money to go to school
Mum, I'm hungry.
Mum!

School
Back of the class,
John's had the cane
Ben's got the dunce hat
Luke's in the corner
Silence!

After school
Wash up
Go to factory
Hair in a net
Off to work
Ahhh!

Night-time
Home again,
Peace at last,
Straight to bed
Start all over again tomorrow,
With dust, blood and cane,
Help!

Abbie Sharp (10)
Whitelands Park School

RICH VICTORIANS

R ich Victorians we are
I n my bedroom lots of rich furniture,
C ook's kitchen is spotless with soap
H owever my education may be good.

V ictorian life is splendid for us
I n our garden the gardener works
C ooking is brilliant
T roublesome governess
O ur facilities are up to date
R iding in our brand new car
I am going to live longer than many
A t home Mum and Dad don't have to work,
N ursery maid is really nice,
S plendid life is for us.

Kathryn Frampton (10)
Whitelands Park School

RICH AND POOR COMPARED

Poor children
Stuck up a chimney
Dirty and lonely
Factory floors picking up wool,
Hungry slaves no food to feed them
Tough and boring, hard, hard work,
Illness need a doctor!
Feeling bad, very sad.

Rich children
Easy life,
Education,
Healthy and clean,
Servants to help cook,
Feels really easy.

Lauren Basham (10)
Whitelands Park School

THE VICTORIAN CHILD

V   ery hungry
I   rresponsible help
C   hildren's life at stake
T   he families in poverty.
O   ver-worked hours
R   ecovery from illness unavailable
I   f unwary could die at work
A   lmost no food
N   othing to eat.

C   hildren ill in bed
H   yperthermia, big risk
I   ndependent children
L   ooking for work
D   angerous conditions.

Should this be a life for a child?

Andrew Green (10)
Whitelands Park School

A VICTORIAN CHILD

As I walked down the dusty lane,
I stumbled wearily,
The door opened as I walked up to it,
My heart drowned in sorrow,
It was my master!
I felt lonely and ravenous
I slowly hobbled up,
'Where have you been?' barked Mr Tup,
I was sick with sadness,
My protest to go up the chimney showed,
It was as black as coal
Cobwebs hung around me as I climbed ever higher,
The filth of my clothes made it difficult,
I was filled with fear and anxiety,
As I reached the top I fell,
I saw my whole life flash before me,
I stretched out my weak arms,
I managed to hold a rut in the wall,
I climbed down and began to sweep away
The soot I had caused that day
Is this the life of cruelty a child should lead?

Raechel Horton (10)
Whitelands Park School

VICTORIAN CHILD

As I walked down the old dusty road,
Sad, cold and hungry
From my days work at the mine
I got home
To my filthy home
I was ravenous
The gruel was on the stove,
Bubbling away in the ancient metal pan
I burned my throat whilst I ate it
It made me sick
I detested gruel
That's all we had
Down in the mines
Cold, dark and lonely
I wish I was a chimney sweep, at least I would get to talk to people
My ma says I'm full of sorrow
I feel sick,
I feel cold,
I feel lonely.

Victoria Murray (10)
Whitelands Park School